6257 £9

G000161471

Edexcel
GCSE MODULAR MATHE
Examples and Practice

INTERMEDIATE

Stage 2

Heinemann

Edexcel
Success through qualifications

About this book

This *Examples and Practice* book is designed to help you get the best possible grade in your Edexcel GCSE maths examination. The authors are senior examiners and coursework moderators and have a good understanding of Edexcel's requirements.

Intermediate Stage 2 Examples and Practice covers all the topics that will be tested in your Intermediate Stage 2 examination. You can use this book to revise in the run up to your exam, or you can use it throughout the course, alongside the *Edexcel GCSE Maths* Intermediate core textbook.

References in the contents list for each section of the book tell you where to find the most relevant paragraph of the specification. For example, NA2a refers to Number and Algebra, paragraph 2, section a.

Helping you prepare for your exam

To help you prepare, each topic offers:
- **Key points** to reinforce the key teaching concepts
- **Teaching references** showing you where the relevant material is covered in both the old and new editions of the *Edexcel GCSE Maths* Intermediate core textbook. These references show you where to find full explanations of concepts, and additional worked examples e.g.

Teaching reference:
(*pp 47–49, section 3.1, 3.2*) —— The first reference is to the old edition
pp 53–56, section 3.2, 3.3 —— The second reference is to the new edition

Where material is new to the new specification there is no reference to the old edition textbooks.
- **Worked examples** showing you how to tackle a problem and lay out your answer
- **Exercises** with references showing you which exercises in the *Edexcel GCSE Maths* Intermediate core textbook contain similar questions. The first reference, in brackets and italic, is to the old edition. The second reference is to the new edition
- **A summary of key points** so you can check that you have covered all the key concepts

Exam practice and using the answers

An exam style practice paper at the back of the book will help you make sure that you are totally exam-ready. This paper is exactly the same length and standard as your actual Stage 2 exam.

Answers to all the questions are provided at the back of the book. Once you have completed an exercise you can use the answers to check whether you have made any mistakes. You need to show full working in your exam – it isn't enough to write down the answer.

Which edition am I using?

The new editions of the *Edexcel GCSE Maths* core textbooks have yellow cover flashes saying "ideal for the 2001 specification". You can also use the old edition (no yellow cover flash) to help you prepare for your Stage 1 exam.

Contents

Heinemann Educational Publishers,
Halley Court, Jordan Hill, Oxford, OX2 8EJ
a division of Reed Educational & Professional Publishing Ltd
Heinemann is a registered trademark of Reed Educational & Professional Publishing Ltd

OXFORD   MELBOURNE   AUCKLAND
JOHANNESBURG   BLANTYRE   GABORONE
IBADAN   PORTSMOUTH NH (USA)   CHICAGO

First published 2002

ISBN 0 435 53541 2

06   05   04   03   02
10   9   8   7   6   5   4   3

Designed and typeset by Tech-Set Ltd, Gateshead, Tyne and Wear
Cover photo: Digitalvision
Cover design by Miller, Craig and Cocking
Printed in the United Kingdom by Scotprint

Acknowledgements
The publishers and authors would like to thank Jean Linsky for her assistance with the manuscript.

The answers are not the responsibility of Edexcel.

Publishing team	**Design**	**Production**	**Author team**
Editorial	Phil Richards	David Lawrence	Karen Hughes
Sue Bennett	Colette Jacquelin	Jason Wyatt	Trevor Johnson
Lauren Bourque			Peter Jolly
Des Brady			David Kent
Nicholas Georgiou			Keith Pledger
Derek Huby			
Maggie Rumble			
Nick Sample			
Harry Smith			
Isabel Thomas			

Tel: 01865 888058 www.heinemann.co.uk

1 Working with number

1.1 Rounding to a number of decimal places

■ You can round numbers to a given number of decimal places (d.p.).
The first decimal place is the first number (zero or non-zero) after the decimal point.

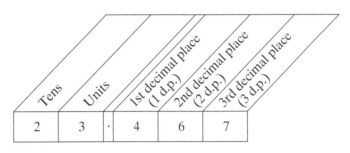

Example 1

Round these to (i) 3 d.p. (ii) 2 d.p.:

(a) 3.6758   (b) 2.3983

(a) (i) In the number 3.6758 the digit after the 3rd d.p. is 8.
          So round up and the 5 becomes a 6.
          3.6758 rounded to 3 d.p. is 3.676.
     (ii) In the number 3.6758 the digit after the 2nd d.p. is 5.
          So round up and the 7 becomes an 8.
          3.6758 rounded to 2 d.p. is 3.68.

(b) (i) 2.3983 to 3 d.p. is 2.398.
     (ii) 2.3983 to 2 d.p. is 2.40.
          (The 8 makes the 9 round up to 10 and this changes the 3
          to a 4.)

> If the number after the d.p. you want is a 5 or more, round up; if it is less than 5 do not round up.

Exercise 1A   **Links (6C) 6C**

1 Round each number to   (i) 1 d.p.   (ii) 3 d.p.:
   (a) 2.3452   (b) 4.8783   (c) 8.4591   (d) 6.3782
   (e) 9.6435   (f) 10.9239   (g) 6.8245   (h) 5.3545
   (i) 11.2395   (j) 20.0608

2 Write each number correct to 2 d.p.:
   (a) 3.678   (b) 5.235   (c) 9.243   (d) 10.494
   (e) 8.695   (f) 12.444   (g) 15.691   (h) 20.348
   (i) 3.995   (j) 0.999

3 Write these numbers correct to the number of decimal places given in the brackets:

(a) 3.261   (1 d.p.)   (b) 4.325   (2 d.p.)
(c) 0.945   (1 d.p.)   (d) 12.3627 (3 d.p.)
(e) 6.063   (2 d.p.)   (f) 4.997   (2 d.p.)
(g) 0.085   (1 d.p.)   (h) 6.894 36 (4 d.p.)
(i) 15.997   (2 d.p.)   (j) 0.0083   (2 d.p.)

1.2 Rounding to a number of significant figures

■ **You can round numbers to a given number of significant figures (s.f.).**
 The first significant figure is the first non-zero digit in the number, counting from the left.

Example 2

Round 746.501 to   (a) 1 s.f.   (b) 2 s.f.   (c) 3 s.f.
(d) 4 s.f.   (e) 5 s.f.

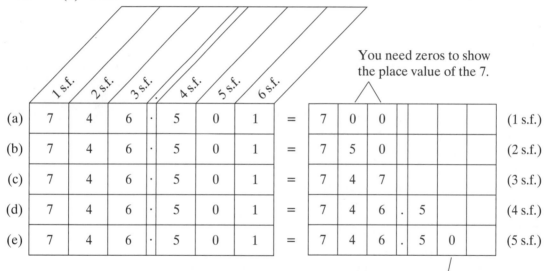

You need zeros to show the place value of the 7.

You need a zero here to show 5 significant figures.

Example 3

Estimate the answers to these questions by rounding all the numbers to 1 s.f.

(a) 17.8×4.2 (b) $234 \div 13.2$ (c) $\dfrac{5.8 \times 7.4}{3.4 + 6.9}$

Rounding to 1 s.f.:

(a) 17.8×4.2 becomes $20 \times 4 = 80$ as an estimate.

(b) $234 \div 13.2$ becomes $200 \div 10 = 20$ as an estimate.

(c) $\dfrac{5.8 \times 7.4}{3.4 + 6.9}$ becomes $\dfrac{6 \times 7}{3 + 7} = \dfrac{42}{10} = 4.2$ as an estimate.

Exercise 1B   Links (*6D*) 6D

1   Write these numbers correct to 2 s.f.:
    (a) 45.6   **(b)** 437   **(c)** 3.682
    (d) 5472.3   **(e)** 0.002 35   **(f)** 0.095

2   Round these numbers to 3 s.f.:
    (a) 945.3   **(b)** 10 678   **(c)** 789 421
    (d) 0.834 52   **(e)** 0.002 3781   **(f)** 0.048 04

3   Write these numbers correct to the number of significant
    figures given in the brackets:
    (a) 4892   (2 s.f.)   **(b)** 78 348   (1 s.f.)
    (c) 378.42   (2 s.f.)   **(d)** 0.028 94   (3 s.f.)
    (e) 2.603   (3 s.f.)   **(f)** 4999   (3 s.f.)

4   Work out an estimate for:
    (a) 72×39 **(b)** $123 \div 19.4$ **(c)** 6.35×2.96

    (d) $7.8 \div 1.89$ **(e)** $\dfrac{23.9 \times 96}{49.6}$ **(f)** $(986 \times 237) + 407$

    (g) $\dfrac{0.28 \times 0.59}{1.01}$ **(h)** 3.14×4.5^2

1.3 Selecting appropriate degrees of accuracy

There are times when the accuracy of your answer must be
appropriate to the question.

Example 4

A teacher orders exercise books for a year group. There are
143 pupils in the year.
Exercise books are sold in packs of 10. How many packs does the
teacher need to order?

$143 \div 10 = 14.3$ packs

If the teacher rounded down, she would have $14 \times 10 = 140$ books,
so 3 pupils wouldn't have a book! So in this case she needs to
round up and buy 15 packs.

Example 5

A unit of electricity costs 4.83p. Work out the cost of 234 units.
Give your answer to an appropriate number of s.f.

$234 \times 4.83\text{p} = 1130.22\text{p}$

As you cannot pay an amount less than 1p an appropriate answer
would be

1130p (4 s.f.)

or £11.30

1 A farmer collects 100 eggs from his chickens. How many egg boxes can he fill if an egg box holds 6 eggs?

2 A car transporter is 8 metres long. It is loaded with cars that are 1.8 m long. How many cars can the transporter carry?

3 Chocolate chip muffins are sold in packs of 4. Mary needs 19 for a party. How many packs will she need?

4 Gas costs £0.019 per kW h (kilowatt hour). Graham uses 297 kW h. Calculate the cost of Graham's bill. Give your answer to an appropriate number of decimal places.

5 Samina drives 184 miles in 4 hours. Work out her speed in miles per hour, giving your answer to an appropriate degree of accuracy. Give a reason for your answer.

6 Luisa wants to draw a circle with a circumference of 60 cm. She calculates the radius to be 9.549 296 59 cm. Write down Luisa's answer to an appropriate degree of accuracy. Give a reason for your answer.

7 £10 is shared equally between 3 children. How much does each child receive? Give your answer to an appropriate number of decimal places.

8 An author receives £0.034 per book that is sold. 17 384 books are sold. How much does the author receive?

9 A wood supplier has a piece of wood 7 metres long that he wants to cut into 6 equal lengths. He calculates that each length should be 1.166 67 m long. Explain why this is not a sensible answer.

10 A cook knows that she needs 100 g of flour to make 6 cakes. She calculates that she needs 133 g of flour to make 8 cakes. Explain why this is not a sensible answer. Give a more suitable answer.

1.4 Simplifying ratios

■ **A ratio is a way of comparing two or more quantities.**

Teaching reference:
(*pp 373–375, section 25.1*)
pp 413–415, section 25.1

Example 6
A recipe for making 12 scones needs 8 oz of flour and 2 oz of fat. These quantities can be written as a ratio.
The ratio of flour to fat is 8 : 2.

■ **A ratio is normally written using whole numbers only in its simplest form.**

Example 7

Write the ratio of flour to fat in Example **1** in its simplest form.

The ratio of flour to fat is $8:2$. To write this in its simplest form divide both numbers by the highest common factor (HCF).
The HCF of 8 and 2 is 2.
So the ratio of flour to fat in its simplest form is

$8:2$ and $4:1$ are equivalent ratios.

$$(8 \div 2):(2 \div 2)$$
$$= \quad 4:1$$

Example 8

Write the following ratios in their simplest form:

(a) $18:12$ (b) $2\frac{1}{2}:1\frac{1}{2}$

(c) $20:15:5$ (d) $1\,m:50\,cm$

(a) $18:12$ HCF of 18 and 12 is 6 so divide both numbers by 6.
     $= 3:2$

(b) $2\frac{1}{2}:1\frac{1}{2}$ Ratios are normally written as whole numbers, so multiply by 2 to remove the fractions.
     $= 5:3$

(c) $20:15:5$ Divide all 3 numbers by their HCF, 5.
     $= 4:3:1$

(d) $1\,m:50\,cm$
     $= 100\,cm:50\,cm$ Rewrite the ratio using the same units then simplify.
     $= \quad 2:1$

Exercise 1D   Links (25A) 25A

Write these ratios in their simplest form:

1   **(a)** $10:5$ **(b)** $27:9$
    (c) $18:9$ **(d)** $8:4$
    (e) $20:10$ **(f)** $36:24$

2   **(a)** $3:6:9$ **(b)** $24:12:6$
    (c) $25:15:10$ **(d)** $10:6:2$
    (e) $12:8:2$ **(f)** $40:30:5$

3   **(a)** $4:1\frac{1}{2}$ **(b)** $6:1\frac{1}{4}$
    (c) $1\frac{1}{2}:3\frac{1}{2}$ **(d)** $2\frac{1}{5}:4\frac{4}{5}$
    (e) $3.2:5$ **(f)** $2.1:6$

4   **(a)** $2\,m:75\,cm$ **(b)** $2\,kg:500\,g$
    (c) $3\,km:250\,m$ **(d)** $2\,min:30\,s$
    (e) $3\,h:1\,h\ 30\,min$ **(f)** $2\,km:1\,km\ 750\,m$

1.5 Writing ratios as fractions

■ A ratio can be written as a fraction.

■ The ratio $a:b$ can be written as the fraction $\frac{a}{b}$.

Example 9

(a) The ratios $8:4$ and $2:x$ are equivalent. Find x.

(b) The ratio of milk chocolates to plain chocolates in a box of chocolates is $2:3$. There are 18 milk chocolates in the box. How many plain chocolates are there in the box?

(a) Writing the ratios as fractions gives

$$\frac{8}{4} = \frac{2}{x}$$

Write the fractions with the same numerators:

$$\frac{8}{4} = \frac{8}{4 \times x}$$

The denominators must be equal so

$$4x = 4$$

so $\quad x = 1$

(b) The ratio of milk to plain chocolates is $2:3$. Use x to represent the number of plain chocolates. There are 18 milk chocolates, so the ratio of milk to plain chocolates is $18:x$.

$18:x$ is equivalent to $2:3$.

$$\text{So} \quad \frac{18}{x} = \frac{2}{3}$$

$$\frac{18}{x} = \frac{18}{27} \qquad \text{(Write the fractions with the same numerators.)}$$

so $\quad x = 27$

There are 27 plain chocolates.

Exercise 1E   **Links (25C) 25C**

---

1 Find x for each of these pairs of equivalent ratios:

    (a) $10:5,\quad 2:x$ (b) $12:3,\quad x:1$

    (c) $15:10,\quad 3:x$ (d) $8:x,\quad 16:4$

    (e) $x:5,\quad 21:35$ (f) $x:42,\quad 3:7$

    (g) $2:5,\quad x:30$ (h) $4:5,\quad x:50$

2 The ratio of boys to girls in a class is $5:3$. There are 15 boys in the class. How many girls are there in the class?

3 The ratio of the sides of a rectangle is $7:4$. The length of a shorter side of the rectangle is 16 cm. Calculate the length of a longer side of the rectangle.

4 The ratio of green sweets to red sweets in a packet of sweets is $4:5$. There are 24 green sweets in the packet. How many red sweets are there in the packet?

5 The ratio of the heights of two similar triangles is $5:2$. The height of the larger triangle is 24 cm. Calculate the height of the smaller triangle.

6 Karen and Keith are paid in the ratio $3:4$. Karen earns £162.60 per week. How much does Keith earn?

1.6 Dividing quantities in a given ratio

■ **Ratios can be used to share or divide quantities.**

Example 10
(a) Divide £15 in the ratio $3:2$.
(b) Jumana, Malik and Hala share £100 in the ratio $5:3:2$. How much does each person receive?

(a) $3:2$ means 3 parts to 2 parts.
So £15 needs to be divided into 5 parts altogether.

$$1\,\text{part} = \frac{£15}{5} = £3$$

so $3\,\text{parts} = £3 \times 3 = £9$
$2\,\text{parts} = £3 \times 2 = £6$

(b) £100 shared in the ratio $5:3:2$

$$5 + 3 + 2 = 10\,\text{parts}$$
$$1\,\text{part} = \frac{£100}{10} = £10$$

Jumana receives 5 parts $= 5 \times £10 = £50$
Malik receives 3 parts $= 3 \times £10 = £30$
Hala receives 2 parts $= 2 \times £10 = £20$

Example 11
$\frac{1}{4}$ of a class are boys. What is the ratio of boys to girls?

If $\frac{1}{4}$ of the class are boys, the class has been divided into 4 parts.
1 part is boys, the rest, 3 parts, are girls.
So the ratio of boys to girls is

1 part to 3 parts
or $1:3$

Exercise 1F Links (*25D*) 25D

1 Divide the quantities in the ratios given:
   (a) 25 in the ratio $3:2$
   (b) 100 in the ratio $7:3$
   (c) £30 in the ratio $4:1$
   (d) £24.60 in the ratio $7:5$
   (e) 350 in the ratio $4:2:1$
   (f) 150 cm in the ratio $3:1:1$
   (g) £240 in the ratio $4:3:1$
   (h) £36.90 in the ratio $5:3:1$.

2 Juan, Gabrielle and Kwame share £200 in the ratio of their ages, $12:8:5$. How much does each person receive?

3 The ratio of men, women and children in a village is $5:4:8$. The population of the village is 3400. How many women are there in the village?

4 The ratio of flour, fat and sugar in shortbread is $4:2:1$. What fraction of the shortbread is flour?

5 The sides of a triangle are in the ratio $3:4:5$. The perimeter of the triangle is 42 cm. Work out the length of the longest side of the triangle.

6 $\frac{1}{5}$ of the pages in a book are printed in colour. The rest are printed in black and white. What is the ratio of colour pages to black and white pages?

7 $\frac{3}{8}$ of a class of pupils catch a bus to school. The rest of the class walk. What is the ratio of pupils who catch the bus to those who walk?

Exercise 1G Mixed questions

1 Round these numbers to the number of decimal places given in the brackets:
   (a) 2.37 (1 d.p.)   **(b)** 4.8764 (3 d.p.)
   (c) 2.695 (2 d.p.)   **(d)** 5.832 (1 d.p.)
   (e) 2.999 (2 d.p.)

2 Write each of these numbers correct to the number of significant figures given in the brackets:
   (a) 37.2 (2 s.f.)   **(b)** 473 (1 s.f.)
   (c) 0.007 52 (2 s.f.)   **(d)** 96 345 (3 s.f.)
   (e) 489.302 (5 s.f.)

3 A flower seller sells roses in bunches of 12. He has 150 roses. How many bunches can he make?

4 Electricity costs £0.059 per unit. Catherine uses 343 units of electricity. Calculate the cost of her bill, giving your answer to an appropriate number of decimal places. Give a reason for your answer.

5 Lucy wants to draw a rectangle with an area of $10\,\text{cm}^2$. She calculates that she could draw a rectangle that measures 3 cm by 3.33 cm. Are Lucy's measurements sensible? Give a reason for your answer.

6 Write these ratios in their simplest form:
(a) $24:6$ (b) $8:4:2$ (c) $1\frac{1}{4}:3$
(d) $2.4:3$ (e) $3\,\text{kg}:500\,\text{g}$ (f) $1\,\text{h}\,15\,\text{min}:2\,\text{h}$

7 Find x for these pairs of equivalent ratios:
(a) $4:2,\qquad x:4$ (b) $x:7,\qquad 20:35$

8 The ratio of two sides of a rectangle is $7:2$. The length of the longer side is 17.5 cm. Calculate the length of the shorter side.

9 Three children share £250 in the ratio of their ages. Their ages are

Rebecca	15 years
Pamela	7 years
Philip	3 years

How much does Pamela receive?

10 $\frac{3}{5}$ of a bag of bulbs are tulips; the remainder are daffodils.
What is the ratio of tulip bulbs to daffodil bulbs in the bag?

Summary of key points

- **You can round numbers to a given number of decimal places (d.p.).**
  The first decimal place is the first number (zero or non-zero) after the decimal point.

- **You can round numbers to a given number of significant figures (s.f.).**
  The first significant figure is the first non-zero digit in the number, counting from the left.

- **A ratio is a way of comparing two or more quantities.**

- **A ratio is normally written using whole numbers only in its simplest form.**

- **A ratio can be written as a fraction.**

- **The ratio $a:b$ can be written as the fraction $\dfrac{a}{b}$.**

- **Ratios can be used to share or divide quantities.**

2 Indices and calculators

2.1 Evaluating algebraic expressions involving squares and cubes

Remember:

n^2 is called n squared or n to the power of 2.	n^2 means n multiplied by itself: $n \times n$.

n^3 is called n cubed or n to the power of 3.	n^3 means n multiplied by itself then multiplied by itself again: $n \times n \times n$.

squaring and cubing are done before multiplying.	$2n^2 + 1$ means work out n^2, multiply by 2 then add 1.

Example 1

Work out the value of
(a) $4x^2$ when $x = 3$

(b) $3x^3 - 2$ when $x = -2$

(c) $\dfrac{4x^2 - 10}{6}$ when $x = 5$.

> Use BIDMAS to help you remember the order of operations.

(a) $4x^2$

$$x^2 = 3 \times 3 = 9 \qquad \text{(Indices)}$$
$$\text{so} \quad 4x^2 = 4 \times 9 = 36 \qquad \text{(Multiply)}$$

(b) $3x^3 - 2$

$$x^3 = -2 \times -2 \times -2 = -8 \qquad \text{(Indices)}$$
$$3x^3 = 3 \times -8 = -24 \qquad \text{(Multiply)}$$
$$\text{so} \quad 3x^3 - 2 = -24 - 2 = -26 \qquad \text{(Subtract)}$$

(c) $\dfrac{4x^2 - 10}{6}$ (Brackets – the line acts as a bracket so work out the 'top' first.)

$$x^2 = 5 \times 5 = 25 \qquad \text{(Indices)}$$
$$4x^2 = 4 \times 25 = 100 \qquad \text{(Multiply)}$$
$$4x^2 - 10 = 100 - 10 = 90 \qquad \text{(Subtract)}$$

so $\quad \dfrac{4x^2 - 10}{6} = \dfrac{90}{6} = 15 \qquad$ (Divide the top by 6)

Exercise 2A   Links (*21B*) 21B

Work out the value of each of these algebraic expressions using the values given:

1 (a) x^3 if $x = 4$ (b) y^2 if $y = -3$
   (c) $3a^2$ if $a = 6$ (d) $2b^3$ if $b = -2$
   (e) $5p^2 - 4$ if $p = 7$ (f) $2m^3 + 11$ if $m = 4$
   (g) $2k^3 + 3$ if $k = -5$ (h) $4t^2 + 7$ if $t = 10$.

2 (a) ts^2 if $t = 3, s = -1$
   (b) pq^3 if $p = 5, q = -2$
   (c) $h^3 + g$ if $h = -5, g = 5$
   (d) $a^2 + b$ if $a = -6, b = -3$
   (e) $de^2 + f$ if $d = 2, e = -3, f = 7$
   (f) $mn^3 + p$ if $m = 4, n = -1, p = 8$
   (g) $j^2 + k^3$ if $j = 7, k = -2$
   (h) $2a^3 - 3b^2$ if $a = -3, b = 4$.

3 (a) $\dfrac{p^2}{2}$ if $p = 4$ (b) $\dfrac{q^3}{4}$ if $q = -2$

   (c) $\dfrac{a^2 + 3}{7}$ if $a = 5$ (d) $\dfrac{c^3 - 5}{8}$ if $c = -3$

   (e) $\dfrac{f^2}{4} + 5$ if $f = 6$ (f) $4 - \dfrac{h^3}{8}$ if $h = -4$

   (g) $a(b^2 + 2)$ if $a = 4, b = 8$ (h) $d(6 - e^2)$ if $d = 5, e = -9$.

2.2 Using a calculator to evaluate expressions

The examples in this section work on Casio calculators. Your teacher will tell you if you need to change any of the instructions.

Teaching reference:
(*pp 438–441, section 30.1*)
pp 490–493, section 30.1

Example 2

Evaluate $3.1^2 \times \sqrt{4} - 2.79$.

$$3.1^2 \times \sqrt{4} - 2.79 = 3.1^2 \times \sqrt{(4 - 2.79)}$$

Press

[3] [.] [1] [x²] [×] [√] [(] [4] [−] [2] [.] [7] [9] [)] [=]

$= 10.571$

> Remember to use BIDMAS to work out the order of operations.

Example 3

Evaluate $\dfrac{8.9 - (2.1 + 3.4)^3}{4}$.

$$\frac{8.9 - (2.1 + 3.4)^3}{4} = \frac{(8.9 - (2.1 + 3.4)^3)}{4}$$

Press

[(] [8] [.] [9] [−] [(] [2] [.] [1] [+] [3] [.] [4] [)] [xʸ] [3] [)] [÷] [4] [=]

$= -39.368\,75$

Example 4

Evaluate $2.1^5 + \sqrt[4]{2.0736}$.

Press

[2] [.] [1] [xʸ] [5] [+] [4] [ˣ√y] [2] [.] [0] [7] [3] [6] [=]

$= 42.041\,01$

> 2.1^5 means $2.1 \times 2.1 \times 2.1 \times 2.1 \times 2.1$. $\sqrt[4]{2.0736}$ means the 4th root of 2.0736.

Exercise 2B   Links (30A) 30A

Use your calculator to evaluate

1 2.1^2 **2** 4.3^3 **3** -2.5^5 **4** $\sqrt{6.25}$

5 $\sqrt[3]{54.872}$ **6** $\sqrt[4]{2.8561}$

7 $\sqrt{11.1 - 3.81}$ **8** $4.2^2 + \sqrt[3]{35 - 6.952}$

9 $2.5^2 \times \sqrt{6.8 - 6.44}$ **10** $(2.3 + 4.1)^2 + (3.8 + 2.6)^2$

11 $\dfrac{(3.8 + 2.4)^2}{5.1 - 2.6}$ **12** $\left(\dfrac{4.5}{2.5}\right)^2$

13 $\sqrt{\dfrac{3.2 + 4.2^2}{0.5}}$ **14** $7.8 + \sqrt{\dfrac{9.2 + 1.1}{3.7 + 2.9}}$

15 $\dfrac{3.8 + 4.2^2}{3.4 - \sqrt{2.9}}$

2.3 Solving equations by trial and improvement

Teaching reference:
(pp 445–447, section 30.4)
pp 497–499, section 30.4

Example 5

Use trial and improvement to solve the equation $x^3 + x = 16$. Give your answer correct to 2 d.p.

Method
Guess a value for x.
Calculate $x^3 + x$ using your guess.
Compare your answer with 16.
If your answer is too small, choose a bigger value for x.
If your answer is too big, choose a smaller value for x.

Keep repeating this process until you find a value for x correct to 2 d.p. which makes $x^3 + x$ as close as possible to 16.

Value of x	Value of $x^3 + x$	Comparison with 16
2	10	too small
3	30	too big
2.5	18.125	too big
2.4	16.224	too big
2.3	14.467	too small
2.35	15.327 875	too small
2.36	15.504 256	too small
2.37	15.682 053	too small
2.38	15.861 272	too small
2.39	16.041 919	too big
2.385	15.951 416 63	too small

You can now see that the answer lies between 2.385 and 2.39.
So $x = 2.39$ correct to 2 d.p.

You must try $x = 2.385$ to find out whether the solution is closer to 2.38 or 2.39.

Exercise 2C   Links *(30C)* 30D

1   Use a trial and improvement method to solve $x^3 + x = 8$, giving your answer correct to 2 d.p.

2   Use a trial and improvement method to solve $x^2 + \dfrac{x}{5} = 17$,

   giving your answer correct to 2 d.p.

3 Use a trial and improvement method to solve $x^3 + 4x = 100$, giving your answer to 1 d.p.

4 Use trial and improvement to solve $\dfrac{x^3}{2} + x = 500$, giving your answer to 1 d.p.

5 Use trial and improvement to solve $x^2 + \dfrac{1}{x} = 10$, giving your answer to 2 d.p.

6 Use trial and improvement to solve $2x^3 + 2x = 50$, giving your answer to 2 d.p.

2.4 Writing numbers in standard form

Standard form is an alternative way of writing very large or very small numbers.

■ **A number is in standard form when it is written like this:**

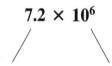

$$7.2 \times 10^6$$

This part is a number from 1 up to (but not including) 10.

This part is written as a power of ten, and the power is an integer.

Example 6
Write in standard form:
(a) 35 600 (b) 2876 000.

	10^6	10^5	10^4	10^3	10^2	10^1	10^0	·	Standard form
(a) 35 600				3	5	6	0	0 ·	3.56×10^4
(b) 2876 000	2	8	7	6	0	0	0	·	2.876×10^6

> The power of 10 is the place value of the first significant figure.

Example 7
Write as ordinary numbers:
(a) 2.3×10^3 (b) 3.78×10^5.

	10^5	10^4	10^3	10^2	10^1	10^0	·	Standard form
			2	3	0	0	·	2.3×10^3
	3	7	8	0	0	0	·	3.78×10^5

> You can think of multiplying by a positive power of ten as moving the digits to the left by the same number of places as the power of 10.

(a) $2.3 \times 10^3 = 2300$
(b) $3.78 \times 10^5 = 378\,000$

Example 8

Write in standard form:

(a) 0.48   (b) 0.0025.

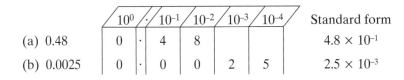

	10^0	$\cdot$	10^{-1}	10^{-2}	10^{-3}	10^{-4}	Standard form
(a) 0.48	0	$\cdot$	4	8			4.8×10^{-1}
(b) 0.0025	0	$\cdot$	0	0	2	5	2.5×10^{-3}

Example 9

Write as ordinary numbers:

(a) 2.4×10^{-2} (b) 5.63×10^{-4}

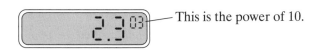

10^0	$\cdot$	10^{-1}	10^{-2}	10^{-3}	10^{-4}	10^{-5}	10^{-6}	Standard form
0	$\cdot$	0	2	4				2.4×10^{-2}
0	$\cdot$	0	0	0	5	6	3	5.63×10^{-4}

> You can think of multiplying by a negative power of ten as moving the digits to the right by the same number of places as the power of 10.

(a) $2.4 \times 10^{-2} = 0.024$

(b) $5.63 \times 10^{-4} = 0.000\,563$

Standard form and calculators

When you do a calculation on a calculator and the answer is very big or very small, the calculator will display the answer in standard form.

Different calculators display the answer in different ways. Two of the most common ways are shown below:

Display 1:

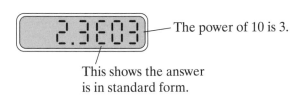

This is the power of 10.

This display shows 2.3×10^3.

Display 2:

This shows the answer is in standard form.

The power of 10 is 3.

This display also shows 2.3×10^3.

You can enter a number in standard form into your calculator.

To enter 5.8×10^4 into a calculator press

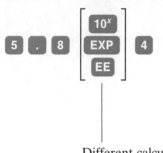

Different calculators
use different symbols.

Exercise 2D ◐ **Links** (*14H, 14I*) **14H, 14I**

1 Write the following numbers in standard form:
   (a) 800   (b) 7000   (c) 90 000
   (d) 872   (e) 9200   (f) 8700
   (g) 98 400   (h) 834 000   (i) 1200 000

2 Write as ordinary numbers:
   (a) 3×10^2 (b) 5×10^4 (c) 8×10^6
   (d) 2.5×10^4 (e) 3.8×10^6 (f) 2.36×10^4
   (g) 4.78×10^6 (h) 2.94×10^5 (i) 3.84×10^7

3 Write in standard form:
   (a) 0.8   (b) 0.72   (c) 0.04
   (d) 0.02   (e) 0.0053   (f) 0.0089
   (g) 0.0032   (h) 0.0485   (i) 0.000 041

4 Write as ordinary numbers:
   (a) 2×10^{-1} (b) 3×10^{-2} (c) 5×10^{-4}
   (d) 2.1×10^{-2} (e) 3.4×10^{-5} (f) 5.8×10^{-4}
   (g) 2.38×10^{-6} (h) 4.39×10^{-8} (i) 2.61×10^{-8}

5 Write, in standard form, the number shown on these
   calculator displays:
   (a)    (b)

   (c)    (d)

6 Use your calculator to work out:
   (a) $2.3 \times 10^4 \times 5$ (b) $4.7 \times 10^{-3} \times 2$
   (c) $5.1 \times 10^6 \times 3$ (d) $8.2 \times 10^{-4} \times 1$

Exercise 2E   Mixed questions

1 Work out the value of:
   (a) $4t^2 + 3$ if $t = 5$
   (b) $5q^3 - 2$ if $q = -2$
   (c) pq^2 if $p = 3, q = -4$
   (d) $ab^3 + c$ if $a = 5, b = -1, c = 7$
   (e) $\dfrac{x^2}{4}$ if $x = -7$

   (f) $\dfrac{y^3}{4} + z$ if $y = -2, z = 7$
   (g) $2a^2 + 5b^3$ if $a = 6, b = -4$

   (h) $\dfrac{4a + 2b^2}{c}$ if $a = 5, b = -4, c = 6$.

2 Use your calculator to evaluate:
   (a) 2.7^3 **(b)** -3.8^2
   (c) $\sqrt{14.44}$ **(d)** $\sqrt[3]{12.167}$

   (e) $2.1^2 + \sqrt{3.1 - 1.89}$ **(f)** $\dfrac{(2.1 + 3.2)^2}{3.2 - 1.3}$

   (g) $2.4 + \sqrt{\dfrac{2.3 + 2.1}{1.1 - 0.3}}$

3 Use a trial and improvement method to solve $x^2 + \dfrac{3}{x} = 15$,

   giving your answer correct to 2 d.p.

4 Use a trial and improvement method to solve $x^3 + x = 800$,
   giving your answer correct to 2 d.p.

5 Write in standard form:
   (a) 3000   **(b)** 5800   **(c)** 789 000
   (d) 86 300   **(e)** 0.5   **(f)** 0.061
   (g) 0.000 21   **(h)** 0.000 381

6 Write as ordinary numbers:
   (a) 2×10^4 **(b)** 2.3×10^3 **(c)** 3.84×10^5
   (d) 8.97×10^7 **(e)** 3×10^{-4} **(f)** 2.1×10^{-6}
   (g) 7.92×10^{-3} **(h)** 8.26×10^{-2}

7 Write, in standard form, the number shown on these
   calculator displays:
   (a) 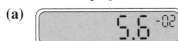   **(b)**

8 Use your calculator to work out:
   (a) $2.68 \times 10^4 \times 3$ **(b)** $3.82 \times 10^{-5} \times 4$

Summary of key points

■ A number is in standard form when it is written like this:

$$7.2 \times 10^6$$

This part is a number from 1 up to (but not including) 10.

This part is written as a power of ten, and the power is an integer.

3 Graphs

3.1 Graphs of linear functions

Teaching reference:
(p 87, section 7.3)

Example 1

Draw the graph of $y = 2x + 3$, taking values of x from -3 to 2.

Here is a table of values:

x	-3	-2	-1	0	1	2
y	-3	-1	1	3	5	7

- $y = 2x + 3$ is the equation of a straight line.

- The coordinates of any point on the straight line satisfy the equation $y = 2x + 3$.

- In general, $y = mx + c$ is the equation of a straight line. m may be positive or negative and a whole number or a fraction.

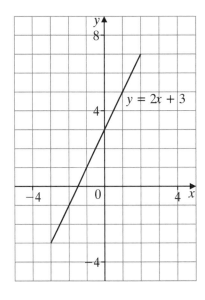

For example, $y = -2x + 1$ and $y = \frac{1}{2}x - 5$ are equations of straight lines.

Example 2

Draw the graph of $y = -2x + 1$, taking values of x from -2 to 3.

Here is a table of values:

x	-2	-1	0	1	2	3
y	5	3	1	-1	-3	-5

- The equation $y = -2x + 1$ may also be written as $y = 1 - 2x$ or $2x + y = 1$.

- If you are not asked to make a table of values, you need only plot two points on a line to be able to draw it, but a third point is a useful check.

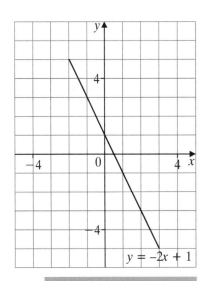

Choose numbers which make your working out as easy as possible!

Example 3

Draw the graph of $x + y = 3$, for values of x from -2 to 5.

For every point on the line $x + y = 3$, the sum of the x-coordinate and the y-coordinate is 3.

So, when $x = 0$, $y = 3$

when $x = 3$, $y = 0$

when $x = 2$, $y = 1$

A table shows the coordinates more clearly:

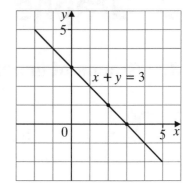

x	0	2	3
y	3	1	0

■ **The equation $x + y = 3$ may also be written as $y = -x + 3$ or $y = 3 - x$.**

Example 4

Draw the graph of $2x + 3y = 12$ for values of x from -2 to 8.

The table shows the coordinates of three points on the line $2x + 3y = 12$.

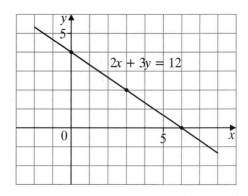

x	0	3	6
y	4	2	0

■ **The equation $2x + 3y = 12$ may also be written as $y = -\frac{2}{3}x + 4$.**

Exercise 3A   Links (*7D*) 7D

1   Complete the table of values for $y = 3x - 2$ and draw its graph:

x	-3	-2	-1	0	1	2	3
y		-8					7

2   Complete the table of values for $y = -2x + 3$ and draw its graph:

x	-3	-2	-1	0	1	2	3
y		7					-3

3 Complete the table of values for $y = \frac{1}{2}x + 2$ and draw its graph:

x	−6	−4	−2	0	2	4	6
y			1				5

4 Complete the table of values for $x + y = 5$ and draw its graph:

x	−2	−1	0	1	2	3	4	5	6
y		6							

5 Complete the table of values for $x - y = 1$ and draw its graph:

x	−2	−1	0	1	2	3	4	5	6
y		−2							

6 Complete the table of values for $x + 2y = 6$ and draw its graph:

x	−4	−2	0	2	4	6	8	10
y		4						

7 Complete the table of values for $3x + 4y = 12$ and draw its graph:

x	−4	0	4	8	12
y					−6

8 Complete the table of values for $2x - 3y = 18$ and draw its graph:

x	−3	0	3	6	9	12
y			−4			

9 Complete the table of values for $y = -\frac{3}{4}x + 1$ and draw its graph:

x	−8	−4	0	4	8
y	7				

10 By finding the coordinates of three points on the line, draw each of the following lines between $x = -4$ and $x = 4$:

    (a) $y = 4x + 1$ **(b)** $y = -3x + 4$ **(c)** $y = \frac{1}{3}x + 2$

    (d) $y = 5 - \frac{1}{2}x$ **(e)** $x + y = 2$ **(f)** $2x + y = 4$

    (g) $x - y = 3$ **(h)** $3x + 2y = 6$ **(i)** $3x - 2y = 6$

3.2 Using straight line graphs for real-life problems

Teaching reference:
(*pp 93–96, section 7.6*)

■ Straight line graphs arise from a variety of real-life problems. Examples are conversion graphs, distance–time graphs and speed–time graphs.

Example 5

This graph can be used to convert between miles and kilometres:

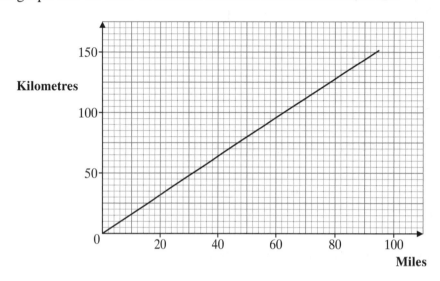

(a) Convert 34 miles to kilometres.
(b) Convert 115 km to miles.

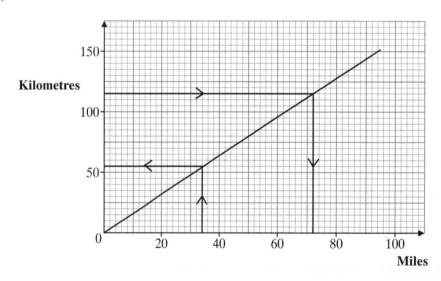

(a) 34 miles = 55 km

(b) 115 km = 72 miles

In examinations, to make your method clear, draw lines on a graph, like those in the example.

Example 6

Here is the distance–time graph for Peter's cycle ride:

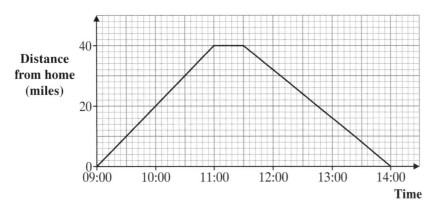

(a) Find Peter's distance from home at 10:15.
(b) Describe the three stages of Peter's journey.
(c) Work out Peter's average speed between
    (i)   09:00 and 11:00
    (ii) 11:30 and 14:00.

(a)

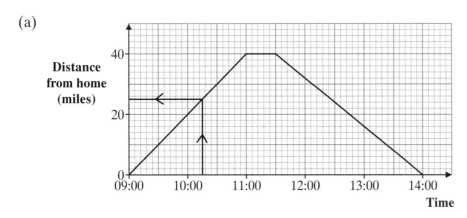

At 10:15, Peter is 25 miles from home.

(b) Between 09:00 and 11:00, Peter cycles 40 miles. His speed is *constant*, because this part of the graph is a straight line.
Between 11:00 and 11:30 (the horizontal part of the graph), Peter is not moving, having a rest and a snack, perhaps.
Between 11:30 and 14:00, Peter cycles 40 miles back home at a constant speed.

(c) Average speed $= \dfrac{\text{total distance travelled}}{\text{total time taken}}$

(i) Average speed $= \dfrac{40}{2} = 20\,\text{mph}$

(ii) Average speed $= \dfrac{40}{2.5} = 16\,\text{mph}$

You do *not* work out $\dfrac{40}{2.30}$.

Exercise 3B   Links (*7G*)

1 Use the graph in Example **5** to
  (a) convert 56 miles to kilometres,
  (b) convert 62 km to miles.

2 This graph can be used to convert between pounds and Swiss Francs (SF):

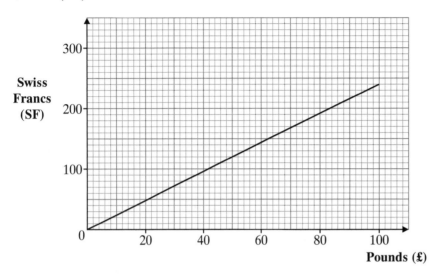

  (a) Convert to Swiss Francs:
     (i) £50   **(ii)** £12   **(iii)** £38   **(iv)** £87
  (b) Convert to £s:
     (i) 100 SF   **(ii)** 130 SF   **(iii)** 210 SF   **(iv)** 185 SF

3 **(a)** 1 kilogram (kg) = 2.2 pounds (lb).
      Copy and complete the table:

Kilograms (kg)	0	10	20	30	40	50
Pounds (lb)	0			66		

  (b) Using a scale of 1 cm to 5 kg on the horizontal axis and a
      scale of 1 cm to 10 lb on the vertical axis, plot the points
      given by the pairs of values in your table. Join the points
      with a straight line.
  (c) Use your graph to convert
     (i) 33 kg to pounds   **(ii)** 42 lb to kilograms.

4 **(a)** £1 = 1.6 Euros. Make a conversion graph for amounts up
      to £50.
      Plot (0, 0) and at least two more points on your line.
      Use a scale of 1 cm to £5 on the horizontal axis and a
      scale of 1 cm to 10 Euros on the vertical axis.
  (b) Use your graph to convert
     (i) £44 to Euros   **(ii)** 37 Euros to £.

5 This rule can be used to work out the time, in minutes, needed to cook a turkey: multiply the weight in pounds by 15 and then add 15.

(a) Use the rule to copy and complete the table:

Weight (lb)	Cooking time (min)
5	
10	
15	240
20	

(b) Draw a graph to show this information.
(You should not join the straight line to the origin.)
(c) Use your graph to find
 (i) the cooking time needed for a 17 lb turkey,
 (ii) the weight of a turkey if its cooking time is 3 hours.

6 Paul drove from Birmingham to Liverpool and back. Here is the distance–time graph for his journey:

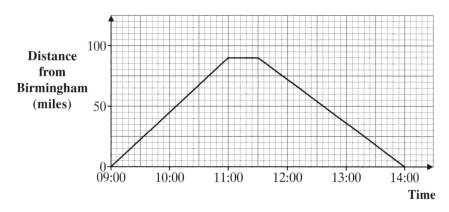

(a) Find his distance from Birmingham at 10:00.
(b) At what time did he reach Liverpool?
(c) For how long did he stay in Liverpool?
(d) Work out his average speed for
 (i) the journey from Birmingham to Liverpool,
 (ii) the journey from Liverpool to Birmingham,
 (iii) the whole journey.

7 Aishya set off from home at 1 pm. She cycled 36 km in 2 hours and then rested for an hour. She cycled a further 12 km in half an hour and finally cycled the 48 km home, arriving at 7 pm.

Assume that she cycled at a constant speed during each stage of her journey.

(a) Draw a distance–time graph for her journey.
(b) Work out her average speed for the whole journey.

8   Here is the speed–time graph for 25 seconds of a train's journey:

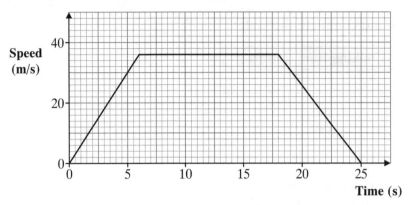

(a)   Write down the train's speed after 4 seconds.
(b)   For how long does the train travel at a constant speed?
(c)   Work out the distance the train travels while its speed is constant.
(d)   Write down the two times at which the train's speed is 18 m/s.

3.3 Graphs that describe real-life situations

Teaching reference:
(*pp 250–254, section 18.9*)

■   **Graphs can be used to describe a wide variety of real-life situations. You may have to interpret or sketch graphs of this type.**

Example 7

Here is a speed–time graph for a car. Describe what happened.

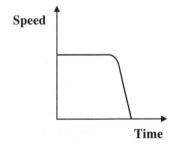

The car was travelling at a steady speed and then stopped suddenly.

Example 8

Sketch a graph to show how the time taken to pick the strawberries in a field depends on the number of pickers.

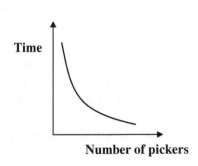

The graph shows that, as the number of pickers increases, the time decreases; although, in real life, if there were too many pickers, they would get in each other's way! Notice that the curve does not touch the axes; if there were no pickers, the strawberries would never get picked and, no matter how many pickers there were, it could not take no time to pick them.

Exercise 3C   Links (*18J, 18K*)

1 Here are speed–time graphs for two cars. For each one, describe what happened.

(a)

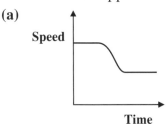

(b)

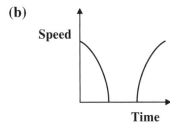

2 Sketch a graph to show how the cost of petrol depends on the number of litres bought.

3 Sketch a speed–time graph for a car which was in a traffic jam and kept stopping and starting.

4 Sketch a graph to show how the value of a new car changes over a number of years.

5 The diagram shows the cross-section of a swimming pool. The pool is filled with water at a steady rate. Sketch a graph to show how the depth of water in the pool varies with time.

6 Vijay invests £1000 for five years. The rate of compound interest does not change in that time. Sketch a graph to show how his investment grows.

7 Marie walks 20 miles. Sketch a graph to show how the time taken would vary if her average speed were different.

8 Graph **A** shows how Derek's weekly wage depends on the number of hours overtime he works. Describe the relationship.

9 Graph **B** is a distance–time graph for a runner. Describe what happens.

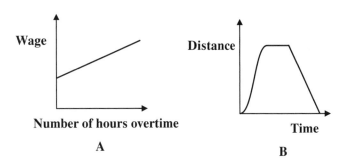

10 Sketch a graph to show how the cost of posting a parcel depends on its weight.

3.4 Graphs of quadratic functions

Teaching reference:
(pp 236–240, section 18.1)

- A quadratic function is one in which the highest power of x is x^2.
  For example, $x^2 + 5$, $3x^2 - 4x + 7$ and $4x^2 + 5x$ are quadratic functions.
- The graph of a quadratic function is called a *parabola*.

Example 9

(a) Draw the graph of $y = x^2 + 3$, taking values of x from -3 to 3.
(b) Write down the minimum value of y and the value of x for which it occurs.

(a) Here is a table of values:

x	-3	-2	-1	0	1	2	3
x^2	9	4	1	0	1	4	9
$+3$	$+3$	$+3$	$+3$	$+3$	$+3$	$+3$	$+3$
y	12	7	4	3	4	7	12

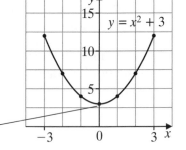

At this point, y has its minimum (smallest) value.

(b) The minimum value of y is 3, which occurs when $x = 0$.

- Graphs of functions of the form $y = x^2 + c$, where c can be positive or negative or 0, all have a ∪-shape.
  The bottom of the ∪-shape cuts the y-axis at $(0, c)$.
  The y-axis is a line of symmetry.

- Graphs of functions of the form $y = ax^2$, where a is positive, all have a ∪-shape.
  The greater the value of a, the narrower the ∪-shape.
  The y-axis is a line of symmetry.

Example 10

(a) Draw the graph of $y = 2 + 4x - x^2$, taking values of x from -1 to 5.
(b) Draw the graph's line of symmetry and write down its equation.
(c) Write down the maximum value of y and the value of x for which it occurs.

(a) Here is a table of values:

x	-1	0	1	2	3	4	5
y	-3	2	5	6	5	2	-3

When $x = 3$
$y = 2 + 4 \times 3 - 3^2$
$= 2 + 12 - 9$
$= 5$

At this point, y has its maximum (greatest) value.

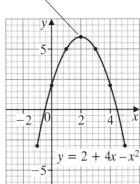

$y = 2 + 4x - x^2$

(b)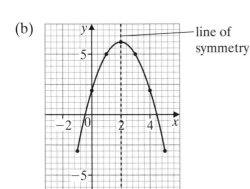

line of symmetry

$x = 2$ is the equation of the line of symmetry.

(c) The maximum value of y is 6, which occurs when $x = 2$.

■ **In general, graphs of functions of the form $y = ax^2 + bx + c$ have a ∪-shape where a is positive and a ∩-shape where a is negative. The parabola cuts the y-axis at $(0, c)$.**

Exercise 3D   Links (*18A, 18B, 18D*)

1 Draw the graph of each of the following for values of x from -4 to 4:

(a) $y = x^2 + 4$ (b) $y = x^2 - 5$ (c) $y = 3x^2$
(d) $y = \frac{1}{2}x^2$ (e) $y = -x^2$ (f) $y = x^2 + 2x$
(g) $y = x^2 - 2x$ (h) $y = (x + 2)^2$ (i) $y = (x - 1)^2$
(j) $y = 2x^2 + 3$ (k) $y = 3x^2 - 8$ (l) $y = 2x^2 - 4x$

For $y = (x + 2)^2$:
when $x = -3$
$y = (-3 + 2)^2$
$= (-1)^2$
$= 1$

2 (a) Copy and complete the table of values for $y = x^2 + 4x + 2$:

x	-4	-3	-2	-1	0	1	2
y		-1					14

(b) Draw the graph of $y = x^2 + 4x + 2$.
(c) Draw the graph's line of symmetry and write down its equation.

3 **(a)** Draw the graph of $y = x^2 - 2x - 1$ for values of x from -2 to 4.
  (b) Write down the minimum value of y and the value of x for which it occurs.

4 **(a)** Draw the graph of $y = x^2 - 4x + 4$ for values of x from -1 to 5.
  (b) Draw the graph's line of symmetry and write down its equation.

5 **(a)** Draw the graph of $y = x^2 + 2x + 3$ for values of x from -4 to 2.
  (b) Write down the minimum value of y and the value of x for which it occurs.

6 **(a)** Copy and complete the table of values for $y = 2x^2 + 4x - 5$:

x	-4	-3	-2	-1	0	1	2
y		1			-5		

  (b) Draw the graph of $y = 2x^2 + 4x - 5$.
  (c) Draw the graph's line of symmetry and write down its equation.
  (d) Write down the minimum value of y and the value of x for which it occurs.

7 **(a)** Draw the graph of $y = 3x^2 - 6x - 1$ for values of x from -2 to 4.
  (b) Draw the graph's line of symmetry and write down its equation.
  (c) Write down the minimum value of y and the value of x for which it occurs.

8 **(a)** Draw the graph of $y = 2x^2 - 6x + 7$ for values of x from -1 to 4.
  (b) Draw the graph's line of symmetry and write down its equation.

9 **(a)** Draw the graph of $y = 9 - x^2$ for values of x from -4 to 4.
  (b) Draw the graph of $y = 7 - x^2$ for values of x from -4 to 4.
  (c) Draw the graph of $y = x - x^2$ for values of x from -3 to 4.
  (d) Draw the graph of $y = 3x - x^2$ for values of x from -2 to 5.

10 **(a)** Draw the graph of $y = 3 + 4x - x^2$ for values of x from -1 to 5.
  (b) Draw the graph's line of symmetry and write down its equation.
  (c) Write down the maximum value of y and the value of x for which it occurs.

Exercise 3E   Mixed questions

1   Complete the table of values for $y = 4x + 5$ and draw its graph:

x	−3	−2	−1	0	1	2	3
y		−3					17

2   Draw the graph of $y = 2x - 1$ for values of x from −2 to 3.

3   (a) Draw the graph of $y = -3x + 5$ for values of x from −2
        to 4.
    (b) Write the equation $y = -3x + 5$ in another way.

4   Draw the graph of $x + y = 2$ for values of x from −2 to 4.

5   By finding the coordinates of three points on the line, draw
    the graph of $x + 2y = 4$ between $x = -2$ and $x = 6$.

6   By finding the coordinates of three points on the line, draw
    the graph of $5x + 2y = 10$ between $x = -2$ and $x = 4$.

7   This graph can be used to convert between gallons and litres:

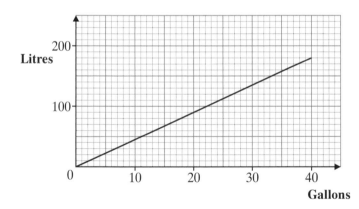

    (a) Convert to litres
        (i)   20 gallons,
        (ii) 18 gallons,
        (iii) 28 gallons.
    (b) Convert to gallons
        (i)   50 litres,
        (ii) 160 litres,
        (iii) 110 litres.

8 Here is a distance–time graph for Mel's motorway journey:

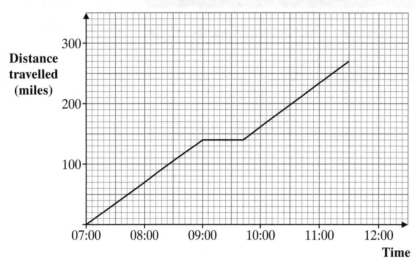

(a) Find the distance Mel had driven by 08:00.
(b) She was caught in a traffic jam from 09:00. For how many minutes?
(c) Work out Mel's average speed for the first two hours of her journey.
(d) At what time had she covered 200 miles?
(e) Work out her average speed for the whole journey.

9 A train accelerates steadily for 3 seconds, increasing its speed from 14 m/s to 36 m/s. It travels at a constant speed of 36 m/s for 5 seconds and then decelerates steadily to rest in 4 seconds. Draw a speed–time graph for the 12 second period.

10 Graph **A** shows how Kate changes the depth of water while she has a bath and Graph **B** shows how the temperature of the water changes while she is in the bath. Describe what happens from when she starts to fill the bath.

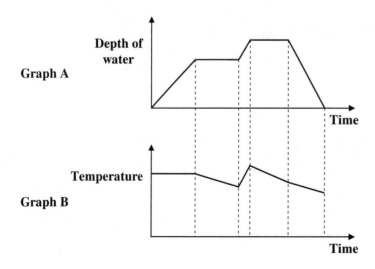

11 The value of a computer falls by an equal amount each year, until, after ten years, it has no value. Sketch a graph to show this.

12 **(a)** Copy and complete the table of values for $y = x^2 + 2x - 2$:

x	-3	-2	-1	0	1	2	3
y		-2					13

   (b) Draw the graph of $y = x^2 + 2x - 2$.
   (c) Draw the graph's line of symmetry and write down its equation.
   (d) Write down the x-coordinates of the points where the graph crosses the x-axis. Give your answers correct to 1 decimal place.

13 **(a)** Draw the graph of $y = x^2 - 6x + 11$ for values of x from -1 to 5.
   (b) Write down the minimum value of y and the value of x for which it occurs.

14 **(a)** Draw the graph of $y = 4x^2 - 20x + 15$ for values of x from 0 to 5.
   (b) Draw the graph's line of symmetry and write down its equation.

15 **(a)** Draw the graph of $y = 2 - 2x - x^2$ for values of x from -3 to 2.
   (b) Draw the graph's line of symmetry and write down its equation.
   (c) Write down the maximum value of y and the value of x for which it occurs.

Summary of key points

- ■ Equations like $y = 2x + 3$, $y = -2x + 1$ and $y = \frac{1}{2}x - 5$ are equations of straight lines.

- ■ The coordinates of any point on a straight line satisfy its equation.

- ■ In general, $y = mx + c$ is the equation of a straight line. m may be positive or negative and a whole number or a fraction.

- ■ Equations like $x + y = 3$, $2x + 3y = 12$ and $3x - 5y = 15$ are also equations of straight lines, as they can be written in the form $y = mx + c$.

- ■ If you are not asked to make a table of values, you need only plot two points on a line to be able to draw it, but a third point is a useful check.

Choose numbers which make your working out as easy as possible!

■ Straight line graphs arise from a variety of real-life problems. Examples are conversion graphs, distance–time graphs and speed–time graphs.

■ Graphs can be used to describe a wide variety of real-life situations. You may have to interpret or sketch graphs of this type.

■ A quadratic function is one in which the highest power of x is x^2.
For example, $x^2 + 5$, $3x^2 - 4x + 7$ and $4x^2 + 5x$ are quadratic functions.

■ The graph of a quadratic function is called a *parabola*.

■ Graphs of functions of the form $y = x^2 + c$, where c can be positive or negative or 0, all have a $\cup$-shape.
The bottom of the $\cup$-shape cuts the y-axis at $(0, c)$.
The y-axis is a line of symmetry.

■ Graphs of functions of the form $y = ax^2$, where a is positive, all have a $\cup$-shape.
The greater the value of a, the narrower the $\cup$-shape.
The y-axis is a line of symmetry.

■ In general, graphs of functions of the form $y = ax^2 + bx + c$ have a $\cup$-shape where a is positive and a $\cap$-shape where a is negative. The parabola cuts the y-axis at $(0, c)$.

4 Working with algebra

4.1 Multiplying bracketed expressions

Teaching reference: pp 299–300, section 21.5

■ $(e + f)(g + h) = e(g + h) + f(g + h)$
   $\qquad\qquad\quad = eg + eh + fg + fh$

Example 1
Multiply out and simplify $(x + 3)(x + 5)$.

$(x + 3)(x + 5) = x(x + 5) + 3(x + 5)$

$\qquad\qquad = x \times x + x \times 5 + 3 \times x + 3 \times 5$ —————— With practice, you should not need this line of working.

$\qquad\qquad = x^2 + 5x + 3x + 15$

$\qquad\qquad = x^2 + 8x + 15$

Example 2
Multiply out and simplify $(2y - 3)(5y + 4)$.

$(2y - 3)(5y + 4) = 2y(5y + 4) - 3(5y + 4)$

$\qquad\qquad = 2y \times 5y + 2y \times 4 - 3 \times 5y - 3 \times 4$ —————— With practice, you should not need this line of working.

$\qquad\qquad = 10y^2 + 8y - 15y - 12$

$\qquad\qquad = 10y^2 - 7y - 12$

Example 3
Multiply out $(3a + 4)(2b - 1)$.

$(3a + 4)(2b - 1) = 3a(2b - 1) + 4(2b - 1)$

$\qquad\qquad = 6ab - 3a + 8b - 4$

You cannot simplify this answer.

Example 4
Multiply out and simplify $(c - 5)^2$.

$(c - 5)^2 = c(c - 5) - 5(c - 5)$

$\qquad\quad = c^2 - 5c - 5c + 25$ ————— Notice that the last term is $-5 \times -5 = +25$.

$\qquad\quad = c^2 - 10c + 25$

Exercise 4A   Links (*21G*)

1 Multiply out and simplify:

  (a) $(a + 3)(a + 6)$ **(b)** $(b + 5)(b + 1)$

  (c) $(c + 2)(c + 8)$ **(d)** $(d + 4)(d + 3)$

  (e) $(e + 9)(e + 4)$ **(f)** $(f + 7)(f + 5)$

2 Multiply out:

  (a) $(a + 4)(b + 5)$ **(b)** $(c + 6)(d - 2)$

  (c) $(p - 1)(q - 4)$ **(d)** $(x - 8)(y + 3)$

  (e) $(a - 9)(t - 1)$ **(f)** $(b + 3)(c - 7)$

3 Multiply out and simplify:

  (a) $(a + 4)(a - 1)$ **(b)** $(b - 6)(b + 3)$

  (c) $(c - 7)(c - 2)$ **(d)** $(d - 4)(d + 4)$

  (e) $(e - 3)(e - 9)$ **(f)** $(f + 6)(f - 4)$

  (g) $(g - 8)(g + 5)$ **(h)** $(x + 6)(x - 6)$

  (i) $(y + 9)(y - 2)$

4 Multiply out and simplify where possible:

  (a) $(3a + 1)(a - 2)$ **(b)** $(2b - 5)(3b + 4)$

  (c) $(4c - 3)(2c - 7)$ **(d)** $(2c - 3)(d + 2)$

  (e) $(5e - 3)(2e - 9)$ **(f)** $(5e + 4)(2f - 3)$

  (g) $(3g + 5)(3g - 5)$ **(h)** $(3x + 8)(4x + 1)$

  (i) $(4y - 9)(4y + 9)$ **(j)** $(2a + b)(3a - 2b)$

  (k) $(4a + 3b)(2c - 5d)$ **(l)** $(7x - 3y)(2x - 5y)$

  (m) $(7p + 2q)(7p - 2q)$

5 Multiply out and simplify:

  (a) $(a + 5)^2$ **(b)** $(b - 1)^2$

  (c) $(c + 8)^2$ **(d)** $(d - 7)^2$

  (e) $(2e + 3)^2$ **(f)** $(3f - 4)^2$

  (g) $(5g + 1)^2$ **(h)** $(7h - 2)^2$

  (i) $(a + b)^2$ **(j)** $(3x - y)^2$

  (k) $(3m + 5n)^2$ **(l)** $(4p - 7q)^2$

6 Multiply out and simplify:

  (a) $7 + (a - 1)(a + 5)$

  (b) $(4b + 3)(b - 1) + 7b - 2$

  (c) $(c + 4)(c - 3) + (c - 5)(c - 2)$

  (d) $(d + 4)^2 + (d - 3)^2$

  (e) $(3e + 5)^2 - 9e^2$

  (f) $(f + 2)^2 - (f - 2)^2$

4.2 Factorizing quadratic expressions

■   **Factorizing is the reverse process to multiplying out brackets.**

Example 5

Factorize $3x^2 - 5x$.

$$3x^2 - 5x = x(3x - 5)$$

x is a common factor of $3x^2$ and $5x$.
So it can be taken outside the brackets.

Example 6

Factorize completely $6x^2 + 21x$.

$$6x^2 + 21x = 3x(2x + 7)$$

The expression has been completely factorized, because the terms inside the brackets, $2x$ and 7, do not have a common factor.

> $6x^2 + 21x = 3(2x^2 + 7x)$ and $6x^2 + 21x = x(6x + 21)$ but the terms inside the brackets have a common factor and so the expression has not been completely factorized.

Example 7

Factorize $x^2 + 4x - 5$.

The factors must be either
$(x + 5)(x - 1)$ or $(x - 5)(x + 1)$.

$$x^2 + 4x - 5 = (x + 5)(x - 1)$$

In other words, find two bracketed expressions which have a product of $x^2 + 4x - 5$.

The first term in each bracket must be x.
-5 tells you that the signs in the brackets are different.
1 and 5 are the only factors of 5.

Multiply out the brackets to find which pair has a product of $x^2 + 4x - 5$.

Example 8

Factorize $x^2 + 7x + 12$.

The factors must be one of these pairs:

$$(x + 1)(x + 12), (x + 2)(x + 6), (x + 3)(x + 4).$$

$$x^2 + 7x + 12 = (x + 3)(x + 4)$$

$+ 12$ tells you that the signs in the brackets are the same.
$+ 7x$ tells you that both the signs are $+$.
The pairs of factors of 12 are 1×12, 2×6 and 3×4.

Multiply out the brackets until you find the pair which has a product of $x^2 + 7x + 12$.

Exercise 4B   Links (*21J, 21K*)

1   Factorize each of these expressions:

   (a) $2a^2 + 3a$ **(b)** $6b^2 - 9$ **(c)** $c^2 - 5c$

   (d) $10d^2 + 5$ **(e)** $ax^2 - 3a$ **(f)** $bx^2 + 2x$

   (g) $5y^2 - cy$ **(h)** $at^2 + bt$ **(i)** $8a^2 - 6b$

   (j) $ab^2 + ac$ **(k)** $3ax^2 - 6bc$ **(l)** $7t - 10t^2$

2 Factorize each of these expressions completely:

(a) $3a^2 + 6a$ (b) $6b^2 - 9b$ (c) $15c^2 - 5c$

(d) $10d^2 + 15d$ (e) $ax^2 - 3ax$ (f) $4x^2 + 8bx$

(g) $cy^2 - 3cy$ (h) $at^2 + at$ (i) $a^2b + b^2a$

(j) $12xy^2 - 8y$ (k) $6a^2 + 9ab$ (l) $3a^2b^2 - 4ab$

(m) $6p^2q + 9pq$ (n) $8cd^2 - 6c^2d$ (o) $4bx^2 + 2bx$

(p) $3ct^2 - 6t^2$ (q) $7ax^2 + 3abx^2$ (r) $5bn^2 + abn^2$

3 Factorize each of these quadratic expressions:

(a) $x^2 + 3x + 2$ (b) $x^2 - x - 2$ (c) $x^2 - 4x + 3$

(d) $x^2 + 6x - 7$ (e) $x^2 - 8x + 7$ (f) $x^2 + 8x + 7$

(g) $x^2 + 2x + 1$ (h) $x^2 - 4x - 5$ (i) $x^2 - 2x + 1$

(j) $x^2 - 5x + 4$ (k) $x^2 - 4x + 4$ (l) $x^2 - 2x - 8$

(m) $x^2 - 9x + 8$ (n) $x^2 + 6x + 9$ (o) $x^2 + 3x - 10$

(p) $x^2 - 8x + 16$ (q) $x^2 - 4x - 12$ (r) $x^2 + 11x - 12$

(s) $x^2 - 2x - 15$ (t) $x^2 - 9x + 14$ (u) $x^2 + x - 20$

(v) $x^2 - 9x + 18$ (w) $x^2 + 10x + 25$ (x) $x^2 - 2x - 24$

4.3 Changing the subject of a formula

Teaching reference:
(*pp 304–307, section 21.7*)

■ A formula (plural: formulae) is a way of describing a rule or a relationship using algebraic expressions.

■ A formula must contain an equals (=) sign.

■ The subject of a formula appears on its own on one side of the formula and does not appear on the other side.

Example 9

Make t the subject of the formula $v = u + at$.

$v - u = at$ Subtract u from both sides.

$t = \dfrac{v - u}{a}$ Divide both sides by a.

Example 10

Make l the subject of the formula $P = 2(l + b)$.

$P = 2l + 2b$ Multiply out the brackets.

$2l = P - 2b$ Subtract $2b$ from both sides.

$l = \dfrac{P - 2b}{2}$ Divide both sides by 2.

Alternatively, you can divide both sides by 2:

$$\dfrac{P}{2} = l + b$$

and then subtract b from both sides:

$$l = \dfrac{P}{2} - b$$

Example 11

Make h the subject of the formula $V = \frac{1}{3}Ah$.

$$3V = Ah \qquad \text{Multiply both sides by 3.}$$
$$h = \frac{3V}{A} \qquad \text{Divide both sides by } A.$$

$h = \dfrac{V}{\frac{1}{3}A}$ is also correct but it's best not to have a fraction within another fraction.

Exercise 4C   Links (*21I*)

In questions **1–30**, make the letter in square brackets the subject of the formula.

1	$P = 5d$	$[d]$	**2**	$P = IV$	$[I]$
3	$A = LB$	$[B]$	**4**	$C = \pi d$	$[d]$
5	$V = lbh$	$[h]$	**6**	$A = \pi rl$	$[r]$
7	$y = 4x - 3$	$[x]$	**8**	$t = 3n + 5$	$[n]$
9	$P = 2x + y$	$[y]$	**10**	$P = 2x + y$	$[x]$
11	$y = mx + c$	$[m]$	**12**	$v = u - gt$	$[u]$
13	$v = u - gt$	$[t]$	**14**	$A = \frac{1}{2}bh$	$[b]$
15	$s = \dfrac{a + b + c}{2}$	$[a]$	**16**	$I = \dfrac{PRT}{100}$	$[T]$
17	$T = \dfrac{D}{V}$	$[D]$	**18**	$T = \dfrac{D}{V}$	$[V]$
19	$\dfrac{PV}{T} = k$	$[V]$	**20**	$\dfrac{PV}{T} = k$	$[T]$
21	$I = m(v - u)$	$[v]$	**22**	$A = \frac{1}{2}(a + b)h$	$[h]$
23	$A = \frac{1}{2}(a + b)h$	$[b]$	**24**	$y = \frac{1}{3}x - 2$	$[x]$
25	$y = 2(x - 1)$	$[x]$	**26**	$x = 3(y + 2)$	$[y]$
27	$H = 17 - \dfrac{A}{2}$	$[A]$	**28**	$y = \dfrac{5 - x}{2}$	$[x]$
29	$3x - 2y = 6$	$[x]$	**30**	$3x - 2y = 6$	$[y]$

4.4 Showing inequalities on a number line

- **An inequality is a statement which shows that one quantity is not equal to another quantity.**

- **You can show an inequality on a number line.**
  An open circle ○ means a number is not included.
  A closed circle ● means a number is included.

$>$ means 'greater than'.
$<$ means 'less than'.
$\geqslant$ means 'greater than or equal to'.
$\leqslant$ means 'less than or equal to'.

Example 12
Show the inequality $x < 1$ on a number line.

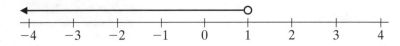

Example 13
Show the inequality $x \geqslant -2$ on a number line.

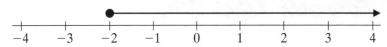

Example 14
Show the inequality $-1 < x \leqslant 2$ on a number line.

Example 15
List the integers which satisfy the inequality $-2 \leqslant x < 2$ and show them on a number line.

The integers $-2, -1, 0$ and 1 satisfy the inequality $-2 \leqslant x < 2$.

> Integers are positive whole numbers, negative whole numbers and 0.

Exercise 4D

In questions **1–12**, show each inequality on a number line.

1 $x > 1$	**2** $x \leqslant 3$	**3** $x \geqslant -1$
4 $x < -2$	**5** $x \leqslant 0$	**6** $-2 \leqslant x < 1$
7 $-1 < x \leqslant 3$	**8** $-3 \leqslant x \leqslant 1$	**9** $-4 < x < -1$
10 $1 \leqslant x < 4$	**11** $0 < x \leqslant 3$	**12** $-1 \leqslant x < 3$

Write down the inequalities shown in questions **13–18**.

13

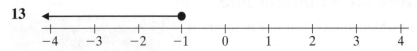

14

15

16

17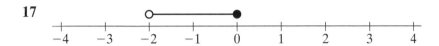

18

19 For each of these inequalities list the integers which satisfy the inequality and show them on a number line:

(a) $-3 \leqslant x < 1$ (b) $0 < x \leqslant 3$ (c) $-2 \leqslant x \leqslant 4$

(d) $-4 < x < -1$ (e) $-1 \leqslant x < 4$ (f) $-3 < x \leqslant 0$

20 For each of these inequalities, list the integers which satisfy the inequality and show them on a number line:

(a) $1\frac{1}{2} < x < 4\frac{2}{3}$ (b) $-3.4 < x < 1.7$ (c) $\frac{3}{4} < x \leqslant 3$

(d) $-\frac{2}{5} < x < 2\frac{1}{3}$ (e) $-0.6 < x < 2.9$ (f) $-4\frac{1}{4} < x < -\frac{1}{2}$

4.5 Solving inequalities

■ **To solve an inequality you can**
  - **add the same quantity to both sides**
  - **subtract the same quantity from both sides**
  - **multiply both sides by the same *positive* quantity**
  - **divide both sides by the same *positive* quantity.**

  but you must not
  - **multiply both sides by the same *negative* quantity**
  - **divide both sides by the same *negative* quantity.**

> You solve inequalities in the same way as linear equations, except that you must not multiply or divide both sides by a *negative* number.

Example 16

Solve the inequality $2x - 1 < 4$ and show the solution on a number line.

$2x < 5$ Add 1 to each side.

$x < 2\frac{1}{2}$ Divide both sides by 2.

Example 17

(a) Solve the inequality $2x + 3 \leqslant 5x + 7$.
(b) Write down the smallest integer which satisfies this inequality.

(a) $3 \leqslant 3x + 7$ Subtract $2x$ from both sides.

$-4 \leqslant 3x$ Subtract 7 from both sides.

$x \geqslant -1\frac{1}{3}$ Divide both sides by 3.

> If $-4 \leqslant 3x$, then you can write $3x \geqslant -4$.

(b) The smallest integer which satisfies this inequality is -1.

Example 18

(a) Find all the integers which satisfy the inequality $-9 \leqslant 3x < 5$.
(b) Show the solutions on a number line.

(a) $-3 \leqslant x < 1\frac{2}{3}$ Divide each term in the inequality by 3.

The integer solutions are $-3, -2, -1, 0, 1$.

(b)
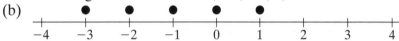

Exercise 4E   Links (*28K*)

In questions **1–12**, solve each inequality.

1 $x + 3 < 7$ **2** $x - 1 \geqslant 5$

3 $2x \leqslant 12$ **4** $\dfrac{x}{3} > 2$

5 $x - 4 < 5$ **6** $5x > 20$

7 $x + 9 \geqslant 9$ **8** $3x - 7 \leqslant 8$

9 $4x + 3 \geqslant 15$ **10** $5x - 7 < 3$

11 $7x - 2 > 3x + 10$ **12** $4x - 3 \leqslant 9x - 8$

In questions **13–18**, solve each inequality and show the solution on a number line.

13 $4x > 11$ **14** $6x \leqslant 3$

15 $3x + 7 \geqslant 1$ **16** $8x - 3 > 7$

17 $2x + 5 < 2$ **18** $7x - 5 \leqslant 3x - 2$

In questions **19–27**, find all the **integers** which satisfy each inequality and show the solutions on a number line.

19 $4 \leqslant 2x \leqslant 8$ **20** $-9 \leqslant 3x < 6$

21 $-15 < 5x \leqslant 5$ **22** $0 \leqslant 6x < 24$

23 $-16 < 4x \leqslant 0$ **24** $2 \leqslant 2x < 7$

25 $-7 < 5x \leqslant 15$ **26** $-5 < 2x < 5$

27 $-10 < 3x < 0$

In questions **28–54**, solve each inequality.

28 $8x < 20$ **29** $4x \geqslant 3$

30 $5x > -15$ **31** $3x \geqslant -8$

32 $\dfrac{x}{4} > -2$ **33** $21 < 6x$

34 $4x - 9 \geqslant 2$ **35** $6x + 7 \leqslant 3$

36 $8x - 1 > 6$ **37** $9 < 7x + 2$

38 $5x + 3 \geqslant 2x + 9$ **39** $7x + 2 \leqslant 3x - 2$

40 $8x - 1 > 5x - 6$ **41** $9x - 7 < 5x + 3$

42 $2x + 9 \geqslant 7x - 6$ **43** $2(x - 3) \geqslant 8$

44 $5(x + 2) > 10$ **45** $3(x + 1) < x + 9$

46 $7 - x \leqslant 1$ **47** $8 - 3x > 2$

48 $2 - 5x < 6$ **49** $7 - 2x \geqslant 3x + 2$

50 $4(x - 3) \leqslant 3 - x$ **51** $10 - 3x > 2x - 1$

52 $6 - 5x \leqslant 2 - 3x$ **53** $3 - 5x \geqslant 4 - 7x$

54 $11 - 2x < 2 - 5x$

55 Solve the inequality $7x + 5 > 4x - 9$ and write down the smallest integer which satisfies it.

56 Solve the inequality $3x + 4 \leqslant 1 - 2x$ and write down the greatest integer which satisfies it.

Exercise 4F   **Mixed questions**

1 Multiply out and simplify where possible:
  (a) $(a + 5)(a + 3)$ **(b)** $(b + 4)(b - 2)$
  (c) $(a + 7)(b + 3)$ **(d)** $(c - 5)(c - 6)$
  (e) $(c - 1)(d + 8)$ **(f)** $(d + 5)(d - 5)$
  (g) $(e - 6)(e + 2)$ **(h)** $(f + 3)^2$
  (i) $(g + 7)(g - 7)$ **(j)** $(t + 9)(u - 1)$
  (k) $(u - 8)(u + 8)$ **(l)** $(v - 6)^2$

2 Multiply out and simplify where possible:
  (a) $(4a - 3)(a + 5)$ **(b)** $(4b - 1)(b + 4)$
  (c) $(4c + 5)(3c + 1)$ **(d)** $(8b - 3)(2c + 1)$
  (e) $(2d - 7)(2d + 7)$ **(f)** $(6e - 5)^2$
  (g) $(2f - 1)(3f - 8)$ **(h)** $(4e + 5)(7f - 2)$
  (i) $(8g + 1)(8g - 1)$ **(j)** $(3h + 4)^2$
  (k) $(8j - 3)(3j + 2)$ **(l)** $(6k + 7)(2k + 5)$
  (m) $(4m + n)(3m - 5n)$ **(n)** $(3x - 2y)(4x + 7y)$
  (o) $(3p + 4q)(3p - 4q)$ **(p)** $(5t - 4u)^2$

3 Factorize each of these expressions:
(a) $7a^2 + 5a$ (b) $8b^2 - 12$ (c) $9c^2 + ac$
(d) $15a^2 - 10b$ (e) $a^2b + 3b$ (f) $d^2 - d$

4 Factorize each of these expressions completely:
(a) $12a^2 - 9a$ (b) $ab^2 - 7ab$ (c) $15ab^2 + 20a$
(d) $6c^2 + 2c$ (e) $3pq^2 - 2pq$ (f) $24xy^2 + 18x^2y$

5 Factorize each of these quadratic expressions:
(a) $x^2 + 6x + 5$ (b) $x^2 + x - 2$ (c) $x^2 - 7x + 12$
(d) $x^2 + 20x + 100$ (e) $x^2 - 7x - 18$ (f) $x^2 - 12x + 36$

6 Make the letter in square brackets the subject of each of these formulae:
(a) $P = ma$ $[a]$ (b) $E = mgh$ $[h]$

(c) $T = \dfrac{kx}{L}$ $[x]$ (d) $T = \dfrac{kx}{L}$ $[L]$

(e) $V = e + IR$ $[R]$ (f) $l = L(1 + at)$ $[L]$

(g) $l = L(1 + at)$ $[t]$ (h) $S = \frac{1}{2}n(a + l)$ $[n]$

(i) $S = \frac{1}{2}n(a + l)$ $[l]$

7 Show each of these inequalities on a number line:
(a) $x \geqslant 2$ (b) $x < -2$
(c) $-4 \leqslant x < 1$ (d) $-2 < x \leqslant 3$

8 Write down the inequality shown on each of these number lines:
(a)
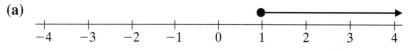

(b)

(c)
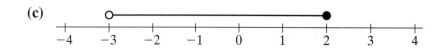

(d)
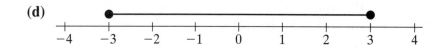

(e)
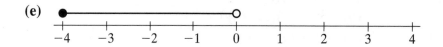

9 List the **integers** which satisfy each of these inequalities and show them on a number line:

(a) $-3 < x < 2$ (b) $-1 < x \leqslant 3$ (c) $-2 \leqslant x < 4$

(d) $-2.3 < x < 2.9$ (e) $-1 \leqslant x < 4\frac{2}{3}$ (f) $-3.6 < x < 2$

10 Solve each inequality:

(a) $x - 6 > 4$ (b) $6x \leqslant 30$ (c) $2x - 5 < 4$

(d) $3x + 7 \geqslant 8$ (e) $5x + 11 \leqslant 1$ (f) $7x - 6 > 3x + 4$

(g) $8x + 9 \geqslant 4x + 3$ (h) $7x - 1 < 4x - 1$ (i) $3x - 1 < 5x$

(j) $7 - 2x \geqslant 3$ (k) $2(x - 3) < 7$ (l) $4 - x \leqslant x + 8$

11 Solve each inequality and show the solution on a number line:

(a) $2x < 5$ (b) $4x \geqslant -2$ (c) $3x - 4 > 1$

(d) $6x + 7 \leqslant 1$ (e) $9x - 5 < 4x + 5$ (f) $6x + 7 < 8x + 7$

12 Find all the **integers** which satisfy each inequality and show the solutions on a number line:

(a) $-6 \leqslant 3x < 7$ (b) $-11 < 4x < 12$

(c) $-4 < 5x < 20$

Summary of key points

- $(e + f)(g + h) = e(g + h) + f(g + h)$
  $$= eg + eh + fg + fh$$

- **Factorizing is the reverse process to multiplying out brackets.**

- **A formula (plural: formulae) is a way of describing a rule or a relationship using algebraic expressions.**

- **A formula must contain an equals (=) sign.**

- **The subject of a formula appears on its own on one side of the formula and does not appear on the other side.**

- **An inequality is a statement which shows that one quantity is not equal to another quantity.**

  > means 'greater than'.
  < means 'less than'.
  ⩾ means 'greater than or equal to'.
  ⩽ means 'less than or equal to'.

- **You can show an inequality on a number line. An open circle ○ means a number is not included. A closed circle ● means a number is included.**

- **To solve an inequality you can**
  - **add the same quantity to both sides**
  - **subtract the same quantity from both sides**
  - **multiply both sides by the same *positive* quantity**
  - **divide both sides by the same *positive* quantity.**

  but you must not
  - **multiply both sides by the same *negative* quantity**
  - **divide both sides by the same *negative* quantity.**

  You solve inequalities in the same way as linear equations, except that you must not multiply or divide both sides by a *negative* number.

5 Pythagoras and trigonometry

5.1 Using Pythagoras to find the hypotenuse

■ Pythagoras' theorem states that in a right-angled triangle the square on the hypotenuse is equal to the sum of the squares on the other two sides.

$$c^2 = a^2 + b^2 \text{ or } a^2 + b^2 = c^2$$

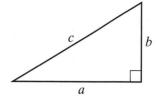

Example 1
Calculate the length of the side f.

Using Pythagoras' theorem $c^2 = a^2 + b^2$:

$$f^2 = 12^2 + 9^2$$
$$= 144 + 81$$
$$= 225$$

So $f = \sqrt{225} = 15\,\text{cm}$

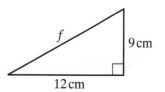

Example 2
The diagram represents a ladder l resting against the wall of a house. The foot of the ladder is 2 m from the wall. The top of the ladder is 7.6 m from the base of the wall. Calculate the length of the ladder.

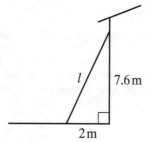

Using Pythagoras $c^2 = a^2 + b^2$:

$$l^2 = 2^2 + 7.6^2$$
$$= 4 + 57.76$$
$$= 61.76$$

So ladder $l = \sqrt{61.76} = 7.858\ldots\,\text{m}$
$$= 7.86\,\text{m to 2 d.p.}$$

Exercise 5A **Links** (*15A, 15B*) **15A, 15B**

1 Calculate the lengths marked with letters in these triangles:

(a)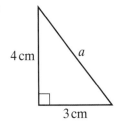

4 cm

a

3 cm

(b)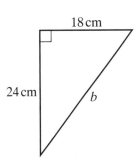

18 cm

24 cm

b

(c)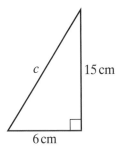

c

15 cm

6 cm

(d)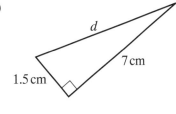

d

7 cm

1.5 cm

2 Calculate the lengths marked with letters in these triangles:

(a)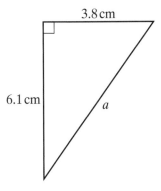

3.8 cm

6.1 cm

a

(b)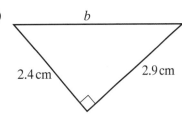

b

2.4 cm

2.9 cm

(c)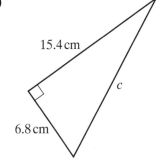

15.4 cm

c

6.8 cm

(d)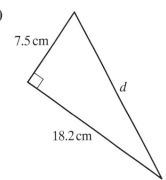

7.5 cm

d

18.2 cm

3   A rectangle is 24 cm long and 15 cm wide.
Calculate the length of the diagonal of the rectangle.

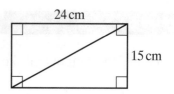

4   A balloon is held to the ground by a cable at point *P*.
The balloon is 10 m horizontally from *P*.
The height of the balloon is 50 m. How long is the cable?

5   Calculate the distance *AD* in this trapezium:

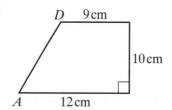

5.2 Using Pythagoras to find one of the shorter sides of a triangle

■   **Pythagoras' theorem states that in any right-angled triangle**

$$a^2 = c^2 - b^2 \text{ or } b^2 = c^2 - a^2$$

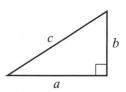

Example 3

In triangle *ABC*, calculate the length *AB*.

Using Pythagoras:

$$AB^2 = AC^2 - BC^2$$
$$= 15^2 - 9^2$$
$$= 225 - 81$$
$$= 144$$

So $AB = \sqrt{144} = 12$ cm

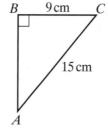

Example 4

An isosceles triangle DEF has $DF = EF = 12.6$ cm and
$DE = 8.5$ cm.
Calculate the altitude of the triangle to 3 s.f.

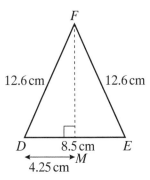

First draw a diagram.
The altitude is the height of the
triangle, FM.
M is the mid-point of DE.

So using Pythagoras' theorem:

$$FM^2 = 12.6^2 - 4.25^2$$
$$= 158.76 - 18.0625$$
$$= 140.6\ldots$$

So $FM = \sqrt{140.6\ldots}$
$$= 11.86\ldots = 11.9 \text{ cm to } 3 \text{ s.f.}$$

Remember to keep the
numbers on your
calculator.

Example 5

A square has a diagonal of 10 cm. Calculate the length of each side
to 3 s.f.

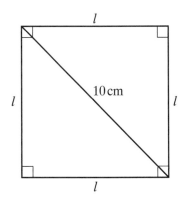

First draw a diagram.
Remember a square has four
equal sides and each of its angles
is a right angle.

Let l be the length of a side. The diagonal is then the hypotenuse
of a right-angled triangle with two shorter sides l.

Using Pythagoras:

$$l^2 + l^2 = 10^2$$
$$2l^2 = 100$$
$$l^2 = 50$$

Divide both
sides by 2.

So $l = \sqrt{50} = 7.07$ cm to 3 s.f.

Exercise 5B   Links (*15C*) 15C

1 Calculate the lengths of the unmarked sides in these right-angled triangles:

(a)

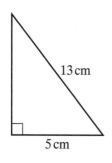

13 cm

5 cm

(b)

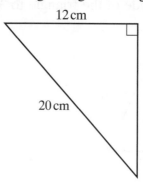

12 cm

20 cm

(c)

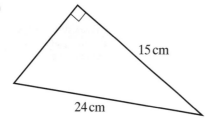

15 cm

24 cm

(d)

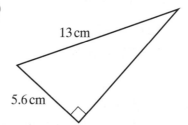

13 cm

5.6 cm

2 Calculate the lengths marked with letters. Give your answers correct to 3 s.f.

(a)

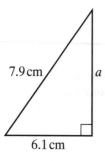

7.9 cm

a

6.1 cm

(b)

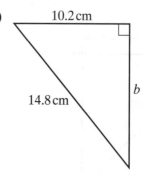

10.2 cm

14.8 cm

b

(c)

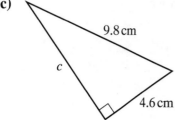

9.8 cm

c

4.6 cm

(d)

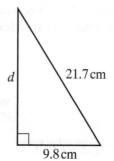

d

21.7 cm

9.8 cm

3 Calculate the heights of these isosceles triangles:

(a)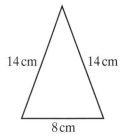

14 cm 14 cm

8 cm

(b)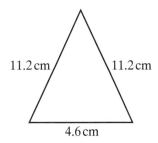

11.2 cm 11.2 cm

4.6 cm

4 Calculate the length of one side of a square with diagonal 12 cm.

5 The foot of an 8 m ladder is placed 2 m from a vertical wall. How far up the wall does the ladder reach?

6 A ramp is made of a piece of wood 2 m long. It gives access to a building whose step is 25 cm high. How far is the edge of the ramp from the building?

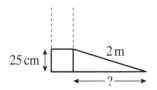

25 cm 2 m ?

5.3 The tangent ratio

■ **The tangent ratio for any right-angled triangle is**

$$\text{tangent of } \theta = \frac{\textbf{opposite side to } \theta}{\textbf{adjacent side to } \theta}$$

or for short: $\tan \theta = \dfrac{\textbf{opp}}{\textbf{adj}}$

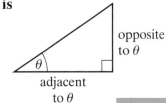

opposite to θ

θ

adjacent to θ

> You need to remember this rule for the examination.

Example 6

Use your calculator to find
(a) tan 29.8°
(b) θ when $\tan \theta = 1.5$.

(a) $\tan 29.8° = 0.5727$ to 4 d.p.

> Make sure your calculator is in 'degree' mode. You normally need to work with four figures only.

(b) $\tan \theta = 1.5$

You need to use the inverse tan function $\tan^{-1}$ or arctan to find θ.

So $\theta = \tan^{-1} 1.5$
$\theta = 56.31°$ to 2 d.p.

> Different calculators use different keystrokes to get $\tan^{-1}$.

Example 7

Calculate the angle a in this triangle:

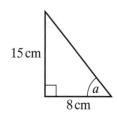

Use $\tan a = \dfrac{\text{opp}}{\text{adj}}$

Here opp $= 15\,$cm and adj $= 8\,$cm

So $\tan a = \dfrac{15}{8}$

$a = \tan^{-1}\dfrac{15}{8}$

$a = 61.9°$ to 3 s.f.

Example 8

Calculate length p in this triangle:

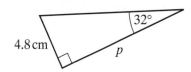

Use $\tan \theta = \dfrac{\text{opp}}{\text{adj}}$

So $\tan 32° = \dfrac{4.8}{p}$

Multiply both sides by p:

$p \times \tan 32° = 4.8$

Divide both sides by $\tan 32°$:

$p = \dfrac{4.8}{\tan 32°}$

$p = 7.68\,$cm to 3 s.f.

Exercise 5C   Links (*17A–E*) 17A–E

1   Use your calculator to find these tangents correct to 3 s.f.:
   (a) $\tan 79°$ (b) $\tan 8°$
   (c) $\tan 51.3°$ (d) $\tan 29.1°$

2   Use your calculator to work out the values of θ, to 3 d.p., if
   (a) $\tan \theta = 1.8$ (b) $\tan \theta = 0.57$
   (c) $\tan \theta = 4.49$ (d) $\tan \theta = 2.6$
   (e) $\tan \theta = 6.19$ (f) $\tan \theta = 0.75$

3   Calculate the lettered angles in these triangles:

(a)

(b)
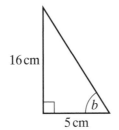

(c)
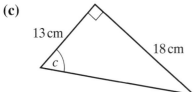

(d)
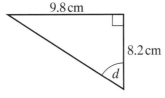

(e)
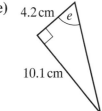

(f)
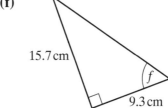

4   Bedford is 16 miles north of Hitchin and 3 miles to the west.

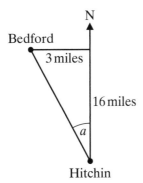

(a) Calculate the angle marked a.
(b) Hence write down the bearing of Hitchin from Bedford.

5   Calculate the lettered lengths in these triangles:

(a)

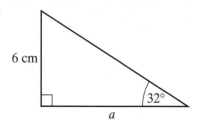

(b)

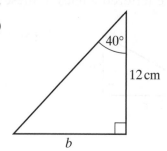

(c)

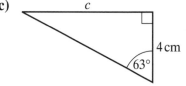

(d)

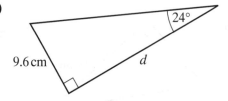

(e)

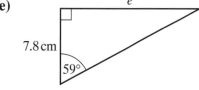

(f)

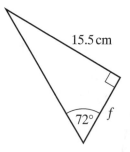

6   A ladder rests against a wall and makes an angle of 71° with the ground. The bottom of the ladder is 1.8 m from the wall. Calculate the height the ladder reaches up the wall.

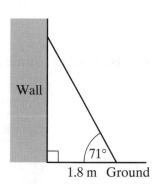

7   Calculate the length of this rectangle:

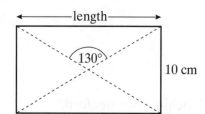

5.4 The sine and cosine ratios

■ **The sine ratio for a right-angled triangle is**

$$\text{sine of } \theta = \frac{\text{opposite to } \theta}{\text{hypotenuse}}$$

Teaching reference:
(*pp 398–404, sections 27.1–27.5*)
pp 446–452, sections 27.1–27.5

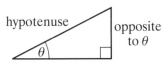

or for short $\sin\theta = \dfrac{\text{opp}}{\text{hyp}}$

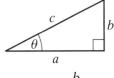

$$\sin\theta = \frac{b}{c}$$

You need to remember this rule for the examination.

Example 9

Calculate the angle marked a in the diagram, correct to 3 s.f.

Use $\sin\theta = \dfrac{\text{opp}}{\text{hyp}}$

Here opp $= 10\,\text{m}$ and hyp $= 16\,\text{m}$; $\theta = a$

so $\quad \sin a = \dfrac{10}{16}$

$\quad \sin a = 0.625$

$\quad\quad a = \sin^{-1} 0.625$

$\quad\quad a = 38.7°$ to 3 s.f.

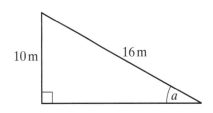

Make sure you use the inverse sine function on your calculator.

Example 10

Calculate the length of the side marked b in the diagram, correct to 3 s.f.

Use $\quad \sin\theta = \dfrac{\text{opp}}{\text{hyp}}$

Here $\quad \theta = 62°$, hyp $= 17\,\text{cm}$, opp $= b$

so $\quad \sin 62° = \dfrac{b}{17}$

Multiply both sides by 17:

$17 \times \sin 62° = b$

So $\quad\quad b = 15.0\,\text{cm}$ to 3 s.f.

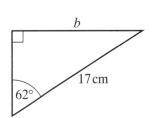

Exercise 5D   Links (*27A, 27B*) 27A, 27B

In this exercise give your answers correct to 3 s.f.

1   Calculate the named angles in these triangles:

(a)

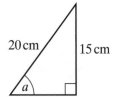

(b)

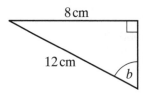

(c)

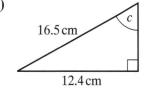

(d)

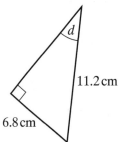

2   In these triangles calculate the named lengths:

(a)

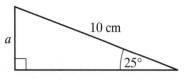

(b)

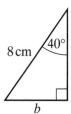

(c)

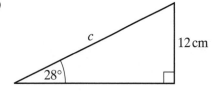

(d)

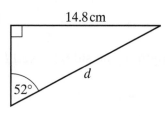

(e)

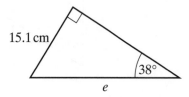

(f)

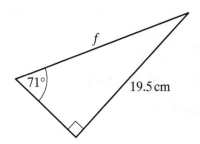

3 Calculate the missing sides in these isosceles triangles:

(a)

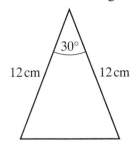

30°

12 cm   12 cm

(b)

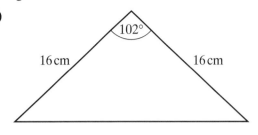

102°

16 cm   16 cm

■ **The cosine ratio for a right-angled triangle is**

$$\text{cosine of } \theta = \frac{\text{adjacent side to } \theta}{\text{hypotenuse}}$$

You need to remember this rule for the examination.

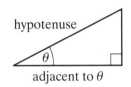

hypotenuse

θ

adjacent to θ

or for short $\cos\theta = \dfrac{\textbf{adj}}{\textbf{hyp}}$

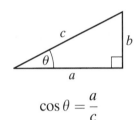

c   b

θ

a

$$\cos\theta = \frac{a}{c}$$

Example 11

Calculate the length a in the diagram:

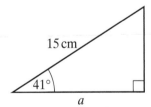

15 cm

41°

a

Use $\cos\theta = \dfrac{\text{adj}}{\text{hyp}}$

Here $\theta = 41°$, hyp $= 15$ cm, adj $= a$

so $\cos 41° = \dfrac{a}{15}$

Multiply both sides by 15:

$15 \times \cos 41° = a$

So $a = 11.3$ cm to 3 s.f.

Example 12

Calculate angle x in the diagram:

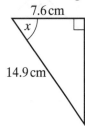

Use $\cos\theta = \dfrac{\text{adj}}{\text{hyp}}$

Here $\quad \theta = x, \text{adj} = 7.6\,\text{cm}, \text{hyp} = 14.9\,\text{cm}$

so $\quad \cos x = \dfrac{7.6}{14.9}$

$\cos x = 0.5100\ldots$

$x = \cos^{-1} 0.5100\ldots$

$x = 59.3°$ to 3 s.f.

> Remember to keep this value on your calculator.

Exercise 5E   **Links (27C, 27D, 27E) 27C, 27D, 27E**

In this exercise give your answers correct to 3 significant figures.

1 Calculate the named lengths in these triangles:

(a)

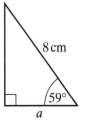

(b)

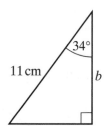

(c)

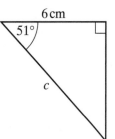

(d)

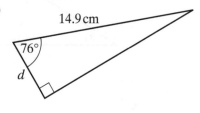

(e)

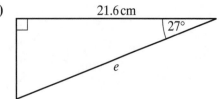

2   Calculate the named angles in these triangles:

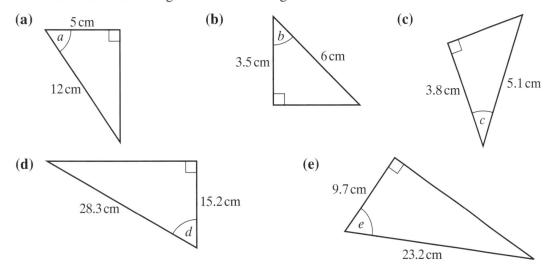

(a)   5 cm
  a
  12 cm

(b) b
  3.5 cm   6 cm

(c)   3.8 cm   5.1 cm
  c

(d)   28.3 cm   15.2 cm
  d

(e)   9.7 cm e
  23.2 cm

3   Martin walks 16 m from the centre of the church, and measures the angle to the top of the tower as 39°.
How long would a rope need to be to go from the ground where he is standing to the top of the tower?

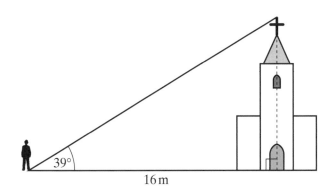

39°
16 m

- **If you look up from the ground to the top of a tower the angle of elevation is measured from the horizontal upwards.**

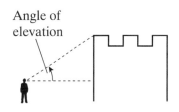

Angle of elevation

- **If you look down from the top of a cliff to a marker buoy in the sea the angle of depression is measured from the horizontal downwards.**

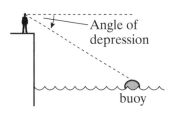

Angle of depression

buoy

Example 13

Morgan stands at the top of a vertical cliff 83 m high. The angle of depression of a yacht in the sea is 32°.
Calculate the distance of the yacht from the base of the cliff.

First draw a diagram:

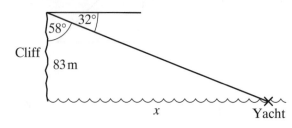

Here $\theta = 58°$, adj $= 83$, opp $= x =$ distance of yacht from cliff

so use

$$\tan \theta = \frac{\text{opp}}{\text{adj}}$$

$$\tan 58° = \frac{x}{83}$$

$$x = 83 \times \tan 58°$$

$$x = 133 \text{ m correct to 3 s.f.}$$

Example 14

Radek walks from point A to point B on a bearing of 049°, a distance of 14 km. How far East and North is he from A?

First draw a diagram:

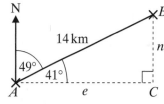

angle $BAC = 90 - 49 = 41°$

To find distance East, e: use $\cos \theta = \dfrac{\text{adj}}{\text{hyp}}$

$$\cos 41° = \frac{e}{14}$$

$$e = 14 \times \cos 41°$$

$$e = 10.6 \text{ km to 3 s.f.}$$

To find distance North, n: use $\sin \theta = \dfrac{\text{opp}}{\text{hyp}}$

$$\sin 41° = \frac{n}{14}$$

$$n = 14 \times \sin 41°$$

$$n = 9.18 \text{ km to 3 s.f.}$$

Exercise 5F   Links (27G) 27G

1   A ladder 9 m long leans against a vertical wall. It just reaches an upstairs window. The ladder makes an angle of 69° with the horizontal ground. Calculate the height of the window above the ground.

2   Bhavana stands at the top of a tower. Proshotam, her father, is on the ground 60 m from the bottom of the tower. The angle of depression of Proshotam from Bhavana is 38°. Calculate the height of the tower.

3   Maxwell runs from point X to point Y on a bearing of 062°, a distance of 25 km. How far
    (a) east
    (b) north
    is he from his starting point?

4   In the diagram, ACD and BCD are right-angled triangles.

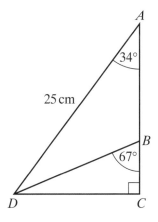

Calculate:
(a) DC (b) AC (c) AB
(d) angle BDC (e) angle ADB

Summary of key points

■   **Pythagoras' theorem states that in a right-angled triangle the square on the hypotenuse is equal to the sum of the squares on the other two sides.**

   $$c^2 = a^2 + b^2 \text{ or } a^2 + b^2 = c^2$$

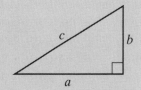

■   **Pythagoras' theorem states that in any right-angled triangle**

   $$a^2 = c^2 - b^2 \text{ or } b^2 = c^2 - a^2$$

■ **The tangent ratio is**

$$\tan \theta = \frac{\text{opp}}{\text{adj}}$$

■ **The sine ratio is**

$$\sin \theta = \frac{\text{opp}}{\text{hyp}}$$

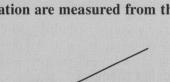

■ **The cosine ratio is**

$$\cos \theta = \frac{\text{adj}}{\text{hyp}}$$

■ **Angles of elevation are measured from the horizontal upwards.**

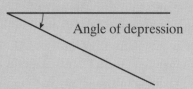

Angle of elevation

■ **Angles of depression are measured from the horizontal downwards.**

Angle of depression

6 Properties of circles

6.1 Tangents to circles

Teaching reference:
(*pp 131–133, section 10.4*)
pp 163–166, section 10.4

- A radius drawn from the point where a tangent touches a circle is perpendicular to the tangent.

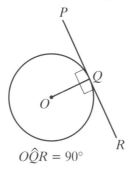

$O\hat{Q}R = 90°$

- Tangents drawn to a circle from a point outside the circle are equal in length.

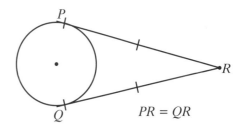

$PR = QR$

Example 1

PR is a tangent to the circle and *MQ* is a diameter.

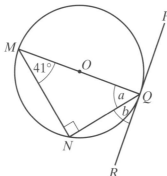

(a) Work out angle *a*.
(b) Work out angle *b*.

Give reasons for your answers.

(a) $a + 41° + 90° = 180°$ (sum of the angles in a triangle)

so $\quad a = 180° - 41° - 90°$

$\quad a = 180° - 131°$

$\quad a = 49°$

(b) $\quad b + 49° = 90°$ (tangent perpendicular to radius)

so $\quad b = 90° - 49°$

$\quad b = 41°$

Example 2

RP and RQ are tangents from R to the circle.

$R\hat{P}Q = 81°$.

Calculate   (a) $P\hat{R}Q$,
              (b) $O\hat{P}Q$.

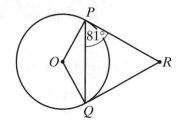

(a) RP and RQ are tangents from R, so triangle PQR is isosceles.

So $R\hat{Q}P = R\hat{P}Q$
                          $R\hat{Q}P = 81°$

Then $P\hat{R}Q + 81° + 81° = 180°$ (sum of the angles of a triangle)

so $P\hat{R}Q = 180° - 81° - 81°$
                          $P\hat{R}Q = 180° - 162°$
                          $P\hat{R}Q = 18°$

(b) $O\hat{P}Q + 81° = 90°$ (tangent perpendicular to radius)
   so $O\hat{P}Q = 90° - 81°$
        $O\hat{P}Q = 9°$

Exercise 6A	Links (*10D*) 10D

In all questions O is the centre of the circle.

1   AB is a tangent to the circle, diameter CD.

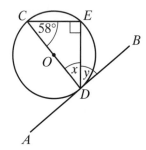

(a) Calculate the size of angle x.
(b) Calculate the size of angle y.
Give reasons for your answers.

2   TP and TQ are the tangents from T to the circle.
Angle $PTQ = 42°$.
Calculate the size of
(a) angle QPT
(b) angle OPQ.

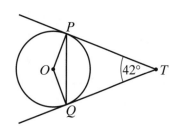

3 *TA* and *TB* are the tangents from *T* to the circle.
$T\widehat{B}A = 67°$.
Calculate **(a)** $A\widehat{T}B$,
  (b) $O\widehat{B}A$,
giving reasons for your answers.

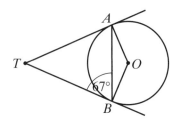

4 *TP* and *TQ* are the tangents from *T* to the circle.
Angle *PTQ* = 54°.
Work out the size of
(a) angle *PQT*
(b) angle *OPQ*.

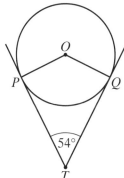

5 *TM* and *TN* are the tangents from *T* to the circle.
Angle *MNT* = 59°.
Work out the size of
(a) angle *a*,
(b) angle *b*,
giving reasons for your answers.

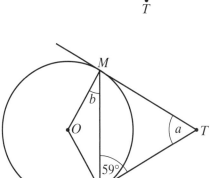

6 *AB* is a tangent to the circle.
DE is a diameter.
Angle *CDB* = 51°.
Calculate the size of
(a) angle *a*,
(b) angle *b*,
giving reasons for your answers.

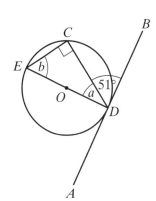

6.2 Area and circumference of circles

- **Area of a circle = πr^2**
- **Circumference of a circle = $2\pi r$ (or πd)**

Teaching reference:
(*pp 277–280, sections 20.2, 20.3*)
pp 308–312, sections 20.2, 20.3

Example 3

Work out the area and circumference of a
circle diameter 10 cm.

$$\text{Area} = \pi r^2$$
$$= \pi \times 5 \times 5$$
$$= 78.5\,\text{cm}^2 \text{ to 3 s.f.}$$

$$\text{Circumference} = \pi d$$
$$= \pi \times 10$$
$$= 31.4\,\text{cm to 3 s.f.}$$

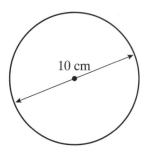

10 cm

Remember the radius is half the diameter.

Use the π button on your calculator or 3.14.

Example 4

Work out the area and perimeter of this pond.
The pond is a semicircle.
Give your answer for the perimeter
(i) in terms of π (ii) numerically.

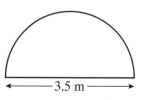

3.5 m

A semicircle is half the area of a circle.

$$\text{Area of pond} = \tfrac{1}{2} \times \pi r^2$$
$$= \tfrac{1}{2} \times \pi \times 1.75 \times 1.75$$
$$= 4.81\,\text{m}^2 \text{ to 3 s.f.}$$

Perimeter of pond = diameter + half circumference of circle
$$= d + \tfrac{1}{2}\pi d$$
$$= 3.5 + \tfrac{1}{2} \times \pi \times 3.5$$
(i) $$= 3.5 + 1.75\pi$$

(ii) Using a calculator = 9.00 m to 3 s.f.

You may be asked to leave your answer in terms of π in the examination.

Exercise 6B   Links 20D, 20E

1   Work out the area and circumference of these circles. Give
    your answer
    (i)   in terms of π (ii) numerically.

    (a)   **(b)**

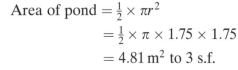

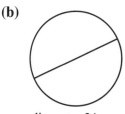

radius 16 cm   diameter 24 mm

(c)   **(d)**

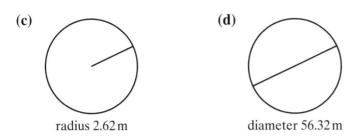

radius 2.62 m   diameter 56.32 m

2 The diameter of a bicycle wheel is 700 mm.
Work out how far it travels in
(a) 1 revolution
(b) 50 revolutions.

3 The diameter of a circular pipe is 15.2 cm.
Work out the area of its cross-section.

4 A circus ring has radius 17 m. Work out its area and
circumference.

5 The circumference of a circular pond is 83 metres. Work out
its diameter.

6 The cross-sectional area of a circular pipe is 2.35 cm². Work
out its diameter.

7 Work out the area and perimeter of these semicircles.
Give your answer (i)   in terms of π
                  (ii) numerically.

(a)   **(b)**

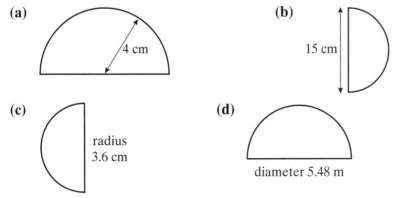

8 A semicircular pond has a radius of 2.5 m. Work out the area
and perimeter of the pond.

9 A semicircular pipe has a cross-sectional area of 14.135 cm².
Work out the radius of the pipe.

10 Work out the area and perimeter of these shapes. The shapes
are made up of rectangles and semicircles.

(a)

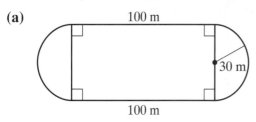

(b)

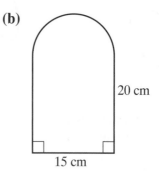

Summary of key points

■ **A radius drawn from the point where a tangent touches a
circle is perpendicular to the tangent.**

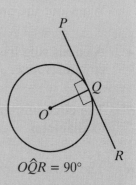

$O\hat{Q}R = 90°$

■ **Tangents drawn to a circle from a point
outside the circle are equal in length.**

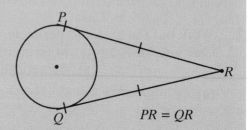

$PR = QR$

■ **Area of a circle $= \pi r^2$**

■ **Circumference of a circle $= 2\pi r$ (or πd)**

7 Translations, enlargements and scale drawings

7.1 Translations

■ **A translation is a sliding movement with no change of shape or turning. It can be described by distance and direction.**

■ **On a coordinate grid a translation can be described by the number of units moved in the x-direction and the number of units moved in the y-direction *or* by a column vector.**

Teaching reference:
(*pp 333–336, section 23.1*)
pp 367–370, section 23.1

Example 1

(a) Translate the shape *ABCD* so that the point *A* moves to the point *P*.

P is the image of *A*.

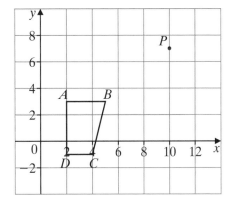

(b) Describe the translation.

(a)

The new position is called the image of the shape.

(b) The shape moves 8 units in the *x*-direction and 4 units in the *y*-direction.

The translation is $\begin{pmatrix} 8 \\ 4 \end{pmatrix}$.

Exercise 7A   Links 23A

1 Draw axes for x from 0 to 8 and y from 0 to 6.
   Plot the triangle $A(3, 2)$, $B(5, 2)$, $C(4, 3)$.
   Draw the image of this triangle after the translations

   (a) $\begin{pmatrix} 3 \\ 2 \end{pmatrix}$

   (b) $\begin{pmatrix} 2 \\ -1 \end{pmatrix}$

   (c) $\begin{pmatrix} -3 \\ 2 \end{pmatrix}$

2 Copy and complete the translation that moves the shape so
   that A' is the image of A:

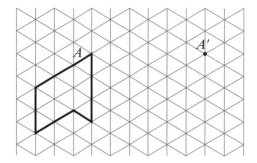

3 Translate the shape so that B moves to B':

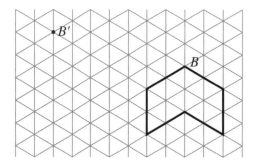

4 Translate the shape so that C' is the image of C:

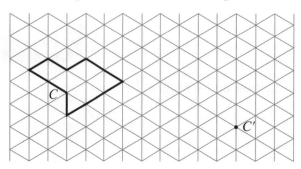

5 **(a)** Describe the translations which map the shaded shape onto **A**, **B** and **C**:

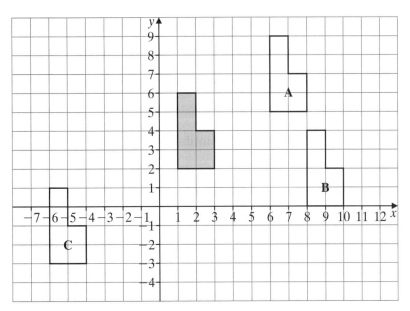

(b) What translation maps **C** onto **B**?
(c) What translation maps **B** onto **C**?

6 Copy the diagram and draw the following translations of the shape:

(a) $\begin{pmatrix} 5 \\ 3 \end{pmatrix}$ **(b)** $\begin{pmatrix} 2 \\ -3 \end{pmatrix}$ **(c)** $\begin{pmatrix} -2 \\ 4 \end{pmatrix}$ **(d)** $\begin{pmatrix} -4 \\ -1 \end{pmatrix}$

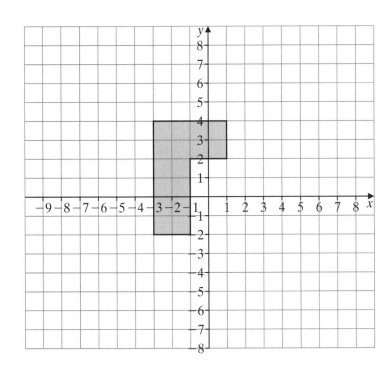

7.2 Enlargements

■ **An enlargement changes the size but not the shape of an object. The scale factor of the enlargement is the number of times the lengths of the original object have been enlarged.**

Teaching reference:
(*pp 343–348, section 23.4*)
pp 377–384, section 23.4

Corresponding sides are always parallel.
Angles are unchanged.
Corresponding lengths are all changed by the same scale factor.

■ **Enlarged shapes are said to be mathematically similar.**

■ **All circles are similar.**

■ **All squares are similar.**

■ **All equilateral triangles are similar.**

Example 2

Enlarge the shape $ABCDE$ by a scale factor of $1\frac{1}{2}$ using the centre P shown:

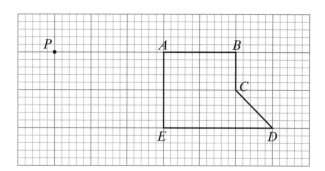

The image of a point will be $1\frac{1}{2}$ times the distance of the original point from the centre of the enlargement.

So $PA' = 1\frac{1}{2}PA$; $PB' = 1\frac{1}{2}PB$; $PC' = 1\frac{1}{2}PC$; $PD' = 1\frac{1}{2}PD$; $PE' = 1\frac{1}{2}PE$.

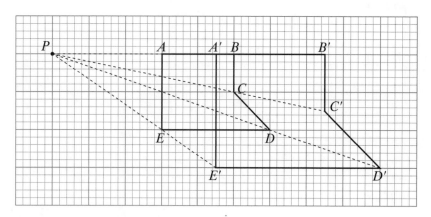

Exercise 7B   **Links 23F, 23G**

1   Enlarge the shape by a scale factor of 2 using each of the
     marked centres in turn:

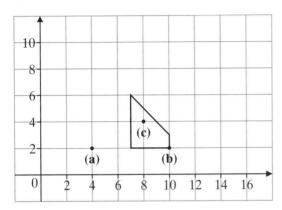

2   Enlarge the shape by a scale factor of $2\frac{1}{2}$ using each of the
     three centres in turn:

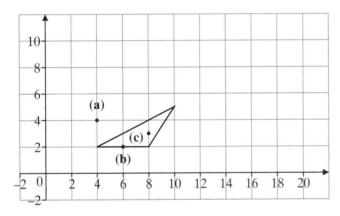

3   Copy and enlarge the shape by a scale factor of $\frac{1}{3}$, using each
     of the 4 marked centres in turn:

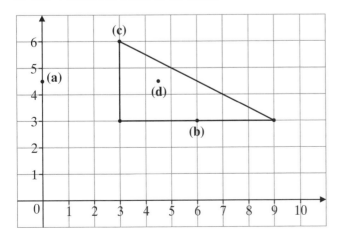

4 In each part give
   (i) the scale factor of the enlargement that maps **A** onto **B**,
   (ii) the scale factor of the enlargement that maps **B** onto **A**.

(a) 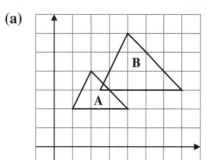 **(b)**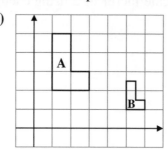

5 In each part find the centre of the enlargement and state the scale factor:
   (a) A → B   **(b) B → C**   **(c) D → B**   **(d) A → D**

> **A → B** means that **A** maps onto **B**.

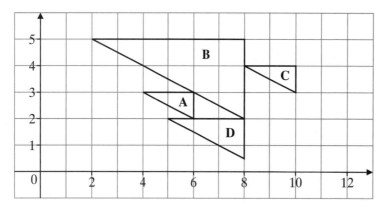

6 In each part find the centre of the enlargement and state the scale factor:
   (a) B → A   **(b) E → A**   **(c) C → A**   **(d) D → E**

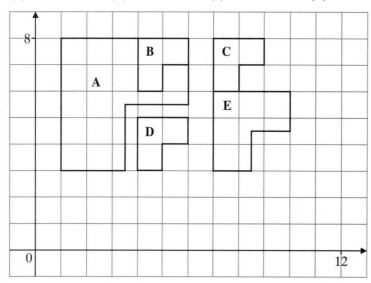

7 Shapes **B**, **C** and **D** above are the same (congruent) and have a perimeter of 8 units. Find the perimeters of A and E, and see how these relate to the scale factors.

7.3 Maps and scale drawings

■ **A scale is a ratio which shows the relationship between a length on a drawing and the actual length in real life.**

The scale may be represented as a ratio (e.g. $1:25\,000$) or in the form of an equivalence (e.g. $1\,\text{cm} = 5\,\text{km}$).

Example 3

The scale of a map is $1:25\,000$.

(a) What is the actual distance between two points which are 5.6 cm apart on the map?
(b) Two places are 9 km apart. How far apart will they be on the map?

(a) Actual distance apart $= 5.6 \times 25\,000\,\text{cm}$
$= 5.6 \times 250\,\text{m}$
$= 1.4\,\text{km}$

(b) $9\,\text{km} = 9000\,\text{m} = 900\,000\,\text{cm}$
Distance on the map $= 900\,000 \div 25\,000$
$= 900 \div 25 = 36\,\text{cm}$

Exercise 7C   Links 26B

1

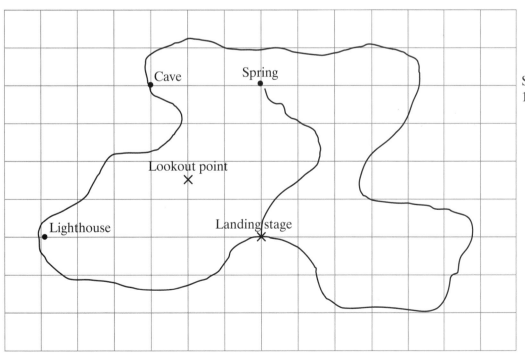

Scale:
1 cm = 2 km

Find the actual distance between
(a) the landing stage and the lighthouse
(b) the landing stage and the spring
(c) the landing stage and the cave
(d) the landing stage and the lookout point
(e) the lighthouse and the lookout point.

2 Copy and complete the distance table:

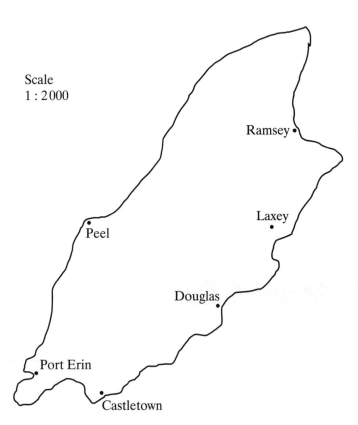

	Ramsey	Castletown	Douglas
Castletown			
Douglas			
Peel			

Scale
1 : 2000

3 Construct an accurate drawing for this sketch.
Use a scale of 1 cm = 5 km.

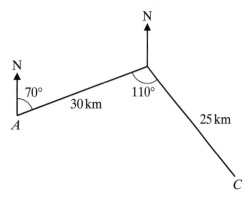

How far is *A* from *C*?

4 Make a sketch and construct an accurate drawing of a journey which consists of 170 km on a bearing of 120° followed by 220 km on a bearing of 050°. Use a scale of 1 cm = 40 km.

5 Make a sketch and construct an accurate drawing of a journey which consists of 66 km on a bearing of 250° followed by 78 km on a bearing of 320°. Use a scale of 1 cm = 12 km.

6 A surveyor's plan has a scale of 1 : 2500.
  (a) A plot of land measures 1 cm by 13 mm on the plan. Work out the actual size.
  (b) A road which is 10 m wide and 125 m long is to be marked on this map. Work out the measurements on the map.

7 The scale of an Ordnance Survey map is 1 : 50 000. On the map Brownsea island measures 4 cm by 2.5 cm.
  Also Bournemouth pier is 4.5 mm long.
  Work out the real distances.

Summary of key points

■ **A translation is a sliding movement with no change of shape or turning. It can be described by distance and direction.**

■ **On a coordinate grid a translation can be described by the number of units moved in the *x*-direction and the number of units moved in the *y*-direction *or* by a column vector.**

■ **An enlargement changes the size but not the shape of an object. The scale factor of the enlargement is the number of times the lengths of the original object have been enlarged.**

■ **Enlarged shapes are said to be mathematically similar.**

■ **All circles are similar.**

■ **All squares are similar.**

■ **All equilateral triangles are similar.**

■ **A scale is a ratio which shows the relationship between a length on a drawing and the actual length in real life.**

8 Mensuration

8.1 Accuracy

Measurements of time, length, weight, capacity and temperature are continuous. They can never be measured exactly.

Teaching reference:
(*pp 160–162, section 12.5*)
pp 198–200, section 12.5

- **If you make a measurement correct to a given unit the true value lies in a range that extends half a unit above and half a unit below that measurement.**

- **Measures expressed to a given unit have a possible error of half a unit.**

Example 1

The length of a piece of string is 53 cm to the nearest cm.

The shortest it could be is 52.5 cm.
The longest it could be is 53.5 cm.
The maximum error possible is 0.5 cm.

Exercise 8A	Links 6F, 12I

In questions **1–4** all measurements are given correct to the nearest unit. In each question, give the maximum and minimum value the exact measurement could be.

1   (a)   72 cm   (b)   16 mm
      (c)   5 km   (d)   100 m

2   (a)   50 kg   (b)   125 g
      (c)   3 tonnes   (d)   82 mg

3   (a)   4 h   (b)   23 minutes
      (c)   7 seconds   (d)   65 years

4   (a)   26 °C   (b)   55 °F
      (c)   750 m*l*   (d)   8 litres

5   In this question the measurements are to the nearest cm. Write down the maximum and minimum the exact value could be.
     (a)   260 cm   (b)   5.28 m   (c)   600 mm   (d)   2000 mm

6   In this question write down the maximum error possible in an answer given to the nearest:
     (a)   hour   (b)   10 g   (c)   15 minutes
     (d)   second   (e)   50 cm   (f)   0.2 seconds
     (g)   25 m*l*   (h)   5 °C.

8.2 Surface area of simple shapes

Example 2

Work out the total surface area of the prism in the diagram:

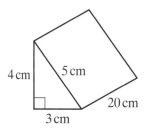

Area of a triangular face $= \frac{1}{2} \times 3 \times 4 = 6 \, \text{cm}^2$

Area of the rectangular faces $= (3 \times 20); (5 \times 20); (4 \times 20)$

Total area of rectangular faces $= 60 + 100 + 80 = 240 \, \text{cm}^2$

Total surface area $= 6 + 6 + 240 = 252 \, \text{cm}^2$

       2 ends   3 rectangles

Exercise 8B

In each question work out the total surface area.

1

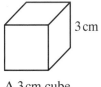

A 3 cm cube

2

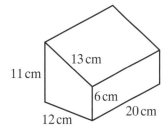

3

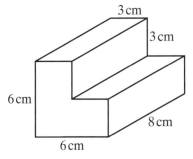

4

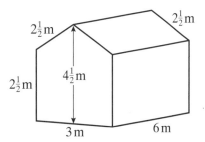

5

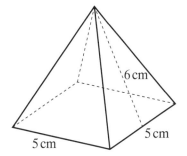

6

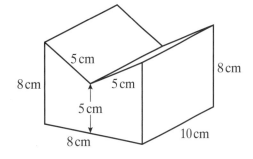

8.3 Volumes of cuboids

■   **Volume of a cuboid = length × width × height**
$$V = l \times w \times h = lwh$$

■   **Volume of a cube = length × length × length**
$$V = l^3$$

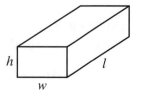

Example 3
Find the volume of the tank shown.
What is its capacity?

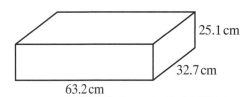

25.1 cm

32.7 cm

63.2 cm

The base measures 632 millimetres by 327 millimetres.
Number of millimetre cubes to cover the base = 632 × 327.
The tank is 251 millimetres high.
This means there are 251 layers of millimetre cubes.

$$\text{Volume} = 251 \times (632 \times 327) \qquad \text{i.e. counting the cubes}$$
$$= 51\,872\,664 \text{ mm}^3$$

$$or \quad \text{volume} = 25.1 \times 63.2 \times 32.7$$
$$= 51\,872.664 \text{ cm}^3$$
$$= 51\,872.664 \text{ m}l \qquad (1\,\text{cm}^3 = 1\,\text{m}l)$$
$$= 51.9 \text{ litres} \qquad (1000\,\text{m}l = 1\,\text{litre})$$

Notice that it is sensible to give the answer to three significant
figures as the information given was to three s.f.
Note also that cm^3 are better to use than mm^3 in this case.

Exercise 8C   Links 20F

In questions **1–6**, find the volume. Give your answer to a sensible
degree of accuracy.

1   A storage box which measures 15 cm by 25 cm by 30 cm.

2   A fish tank which measures 42.2 cm by 20.8 cm by 17.3 cm.

3   A petrol tank which measures 83.1 cm by 45.1 cm by 23.9 cm.

4   A swimming pool which measures 6.32 m by 24.91 m by 1.64 m.

5   A stack of 500 sheets of paper. Each sheet measures 29.7 cm
    by 21 cm and is 0.1 mm thick.

6   A cutting board which measures 25 cm by 35 cm by 6 mm.

7   Copy and complete the table:

	Length	Width	Height	Volume
(a)	4 cm	5 cm		80 cm³
(b)	12 cm		3 cm	216 cm³
(c)	1.6 m	10 cm		6400 cm³
(d)	15 cm		20 mm	15 cm³
(e)		15 cm	2.2 m	1.32 m³
(f)		2.5 cm	6 mm	10.5 cm³
(g)		15 mm	5 cm	0.0018 m³
(h)	3 m	75 mm		6750 cm³

8   A cornflake packet measures 7 cm by 23 cm by 29 cm. How many packets will fit into a carton which measures 58 cm by 46 cm by 63 cm?

9   A packet of pencils measures 14 cm by 5 cm by 1 cm. What would be a sensible size for a box to contain 144 packets?

10   A box of chocolates measures 3 cm by 18 cm by 12 cm. How many can be packed into a carton which measures 30 cm by 36 cm by 54 cm?

8.4 Volumes of prisms and composite shapes

Teaching reference:
(*pp 281–284, section 20.4*)
pp 312–316, section 20.4

■   **Volume of a prism = area of cross-section × length**

Example 4
Find the volume of the length of gutter shown:

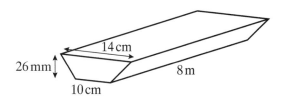

First, choose which units to work in.
In this case, use centimetres.
26 mm = 2.6 cm, 8 m = 800 cm.

$$\text{Area of cross-section (a trapezium)} = \tfrac{1}{2}(14 + 10) \times 2.6$$
$$\text{Volume} = 800 \times \tfrac{1}{2}(14 + 10) \times 2.6$$
$$= 24\,960 \text{ cm}^3$$

Exercise 8D   Links 20F

1   Work out the volume of the first four shapes in Exercise **8B**.

In questions **2–5**, work out the volumes of the shapes shown.

2

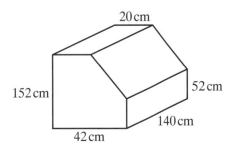

3

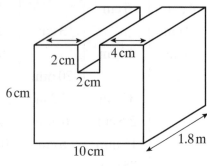

4

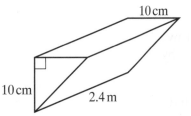

5

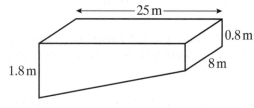

8.5 Surface area and volume of cylinders

Teaching reference:
p 313, section 20.4

A cylinder is also a prism.

■ **The curved surface area of a cylinder is $2\pi rh$.**

■ **The total surface area of a cylinder is $2\pi rh + 2\pi r^2$.**

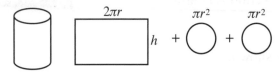

■ **The volume of a cylinder is $\pi r^2 h$ cross section × height**

Exercise 8E   Links 20G

1   Work out the area of the curved surface of a cylinder with
radius 5 cm and length 12 cm.

2   For each of the following cylinders work out:
  (i)   the curved surface area
  (ii) the total surface area
  (iii) the volume.
  (a)   radius 4.5 cm, length 225 cm   **(b)**   radius 12 mm, length 2 m
  (c)   diameter 15 mm, length 6 cm   **(d)**   diameter 3 cm, length 4 mm

3 The volume of a cylinder is 224 cm³. Its radius is 6 cm. Work out its length.

4 The length of a cylinder is 40 cm. Its volume is 50 cm³. Work out its radius.

5 A cylindrical wire is 1.5 km long. Its diameter is 8 mm. Work out its volume.

8.6 Speed and density

Teaching reference:
(*pp 163–166, section 12.7*)
pp 201–204, section 12.7

■ **Average speed** $= \dfrac{\text{total distance travelled}}{\text{total time taken}}$

$$\text{Speed} = \frac{\text{distance}}{\text{time}}$$

Common units m s⁻¹ (metres per second), km h⁻¹ (km per hour)

m s⁻¹ can also be written m/s, g cm⁻³ can also be written g/cm³, and so on.

■ **Density** $= \dfrac{\text{mass}}{\text{volume}}$

Common units g cm⁻³ (g per cm³), kg m⁻³ (kg per m³)

Example 5

An athlete runs 100 metres in 10.2 seconds. What is his average speed in km per hour?

$$\text{Speed} = \frac{\text{distance}}{\text{time}} = \frac{100}{10.2} = 9.8 \,\text{m s}^{-1}$$

$$= 9.8 \,\text{metres per second}$$

$$= 0.0098 \,\text{kilometres per second} \qquad (1000 \,\text{m} = 1 \,\text{km})$$

$$= 3600 \times 0.0098 \,\text{kilometres per hour} \qquad (3600 \,\text{s} = 1 \,\text{hour})$$

$$= 35.29 \,\text{km h}^{-1}$$

Example 6

The density of wood is 0.8 g per cubic centimetre. What is the mass of a post measuring 1.8 m by 75 mm by 75 mm?

It is best to work in centimetres.
1.8 m = 180 cm and 75 mm = 7.5 cm.

$$\text{Volume} = 180 \times 7.5 \times 7.5$$

$$\text{Mass} = 0.8 \times (180 \times 7.5 \times 7.5) = 8100 \,\text{g}$$

$$= 8.1 \,\text{kg}$$

1 Myfanwy drives the 120 km from her home to Bristol in 3 hours. Work out her average speed.

2 Errol cycles for $2\frac{1}{2}$ hours at an average speed of 18 kph (km per hour). How far does he travel?

3 The distance from London to York by rail is 300 km. The fastest train takes 1 hour 50 minutes for the journey. What is the average speed of this train?

4 The speed of a shell fired from a gun is $1800\,\mathrm{m\,s^{-1}}$. How far does it travel in 1 minute?

5 A Formula 1 racing car completes a 6.3 km lap in 1 minute 16.2 seconds. Work out the average speed in
   (a) $\mathrm{m\,s^{-1}}$
   (b) km per hour.

6 The time gap between the first and second cars in a Grand Prix was 3.146 seconds. Assuming the cars were travelling at 305 kph at the finish, work out how far apart they were.

7 The density of iron is 7.86 g per $\mathrm{cm^3}$. An iron bar has a mass of 6.32 kg. What is its volume?

8 A sheet of glass measures 500 mm by 400 mm by 6 mm. It has a mass of 3 kg. What is the density of the glass?

9 A decorative lamp is to be filled with glycerine. Its volume is $72\,\mathrm{cm^3}$ and the density of the glycerine is 1.27 g per $\mathrm{cm^3}$. What mass of glycerine is required?

10 Copy and complete the table:

Substance	Mass	Volume	Density
Hydrogen		$1\,\mathrm{km^3}$	$0.0009\,\mathrm{g/cm^3}$
Air	20 kg		$0.0013\,\mathrm{g/cm^3}$
Aluminium	15.3 kg	$41\,300\,\mathrm{cm^3}$	

11 The density of silver is $10.5\,\mathrm{g/cm^3}$. To check whether a dish is solid silver it is weighed and its volume found by immersing the dish in water and measuring the water displaced. The volume is $52.3\,\mathrm{cm^3}$ and its mass is 611 g. Is the dish likely to be solid silver?

12 A ring is made from gold with a diamond. The ring has volume $0.95\,\mathrm{cm^3}$. The gold is known to have a mass of 15 g. The density of the gold is $19.3\,\mathrm{g/cm^3}$. Work out the volume of the diamond.

Summary of key points

■ Measures expressed to a given unit have a possible error of half a unit.

■ Volume of a cuboid = length × width × height
$$V = l \times w \times h = lwh$$

■ Volume of a cube = length × length × length
$$V = l^3$$

■ Volume of a prism = area of cross-section × length

■ $\text{Speed} = \dfrac{\text{distance}}{\text{time}}$

■ $\text{Density} = \dfrac{\text{mass}}{\text{volume}}$

■ The curved surface area of a cylinder is $2\pi rh$.

■ The total surface area of a cylinder is $2\pi rh + 2\pi r^2$.

■ The volume of a cylinder is $\pi r^2 h$ (cross-section × height).

9 Probability and scatter graphs

9.1 Probability

Teaching reference: pp 298–303, sections 19.1, 19.2

- You must write a probability as a fraction, a decimal or a percentage.

- When one outcome prevents another outcome from happening, the outcomes are mutually exclusive.

- The probabilities of all the possible mutually exclusive events (or outcomes) add up to 1.

- In general, if A and B are mutually exclusive then
  $P(A \text{ or } B) = P(A) + P(B)$.

- The calculated probability of an event happening
  $$= \frac{\text{number of successful outcomes}}{\text{total number of possible outcomes}}$$

- If the probability of an event happening is p then the probability of it not happening is $1 - p$.

- If there are n mutually exclusive events all equally likely the probability of one event happening is $\frac{1}{n}$.

- If there are n mutually exclusive outcomes and a successful outcomes the probability of a successful outcome is $\frac{a}{n}$.

- The estimated probability of an event in a game or experiment
  $$= \frac{\text{number of successful trials}}{\text{total number of trials}}$$
  and this is sometimes called the *relative frequency*.

- The relative frequency, or estimated probability, becomes a better estimate as the total number of trials increases.

Example 1

The four candidates standing in the local election are named

Jones, **Robinson**, **Smith** and **Younis**.

Shortly before the election, a market research company asks a random sample of 1000 voters the following question:

'For which candidate do you intend to vote in the forthcoming election?'

The responses to this question are listed below:

Name	Jones	Robinson	Smith	Younis
Number of voters	28	286	204	482

It is estimated that in the actual election 24 600 votes will be cast.

(a) Work out, with reasons, an estimate for the likely number of votes to be cast for Younis.

A voter is chosen at random.

(b) Work out, with a reason, the probability that this voter **will not** vote for Robinson.

(a) Using relative frequency, the probability of a vote being cast for Younis is $482/1000 = 0.482$.

$$\text{i.e. } P(\text{Younis}) = 0.482 \quad \text{(best available estimate)}$$

Now assuming that 24 600 votes are cast in the election,

$$P(\text{Younis}) = \frac{\text{number of votes cast for Younis}}{24\,600 \text{ (i.e. total votes cast)}}$$

Using the best available estimate for $P(\text{Younis})$:

$$0.482 = \frac{\text{number of votes cast for Younis}}{24\,600}$$

Rearranging gives

$$\text{number of votes cast for Younis} = 24\,600 \times 0.482$$
$$= 11\,857.2$$

Since the number of votes must be a whole number, we round this figure to give

best estimate for the number of votes cast for Younis $= 11\,857$

(b) The estimate for the probability of a vote being cast for Robinson $= 286/1000 = 0.286$.

So the estimate for the probability of a vote **not** being cast for Robinson $= 1 - 0.286 = 0.714$.

Example 2

The diagram represents a spinner.
The spinner is thought to be biased.

Angela spins the spinner 100 times and records the letter it stops on. Her results are listed below:

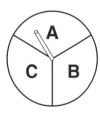

Letter	Frequency
A	42
B	28
C	30

Yousef then spins the spinner 100 times and records the letter it stops on. His results are listed below:

Letter	Frequency
A	38
B	26
C	36

(a) Explain why there is a difference between Angela's results and Yousef's results.
(b) Work out the **best** estimates for the probability of the spinner stopping on each of the three letters.
(c) Explain whether or not the evidence supports the view that the spinner is biased.

(a) Spinning the spinner is an event governed by the laws of chance so its outcomes will be determined by the laws of probability. Therefore when an experiment – such as spinning the spinner – is repeated it is likely that the sets of outcomes – in terms of the number of times it stops on each of the faces – will be different.

(b) The best estimates for the required probabilities will come from pooling all 200 results, since this increases the number of trials. Doing this creates the new, pooled frequency table:

Letter	Frequency
A	$42 + 38 = 80$
B	$28 + 26 = 54$
C	$30 + 36 = 66$

Now we have as best estimates:

$$P(A) = 80/200 = 0.4 \qquad P(B) = 54/200 = 0.27$$
$$P(C) = 66/200 = 0.33$$

(c) If the spinner was not biased, we would have
$$P(A) = P(B) = P(C) = \tfrac{1}{3} \text{ (or } 0.33)$$

Since our calculations give
$$P(A) = 0.4 \qquad\qquad P(B) = 0.27$$
$$P(C) = 0.33$$

it appears that the spinner is biased in favour of stopping on A.

Exercise 9A   Links 3B, 3C, 3D, 19B, 19C

1   An ordinary unbiased cubical dice has its faces labelled with
the whole numbers from 1 to 6.

The dice is to be rolled 1200 times.
Work out an estimate of the most likely
number of times it will land with
(a) the number 5 on its uppermost face
(b) an odd number on its uppermost face
(c) a number **less than** 3 on its uppermost face.

2   A market research team conducts a survey into the normal
method of travelling to school by Year 11 students.

They choose a random sample of 1200 students taken from all
types of school across the country. The results of the survey
are shown in the table below:

Method of travel	Walk	Car	Train	Cycle	Bus	Boarders (no travel)
Frequency	455	206	124	60	347	8

(a) Work out the best estimate for the probability that
someone, chosen at random,
  (i) will normally travel to school by train,
  (ii) will normally **not** travel to school by train.

There is a total of approximately 700 000 students in Year 11.

(b) Work out the estimate of the most likely number of Year
11 students who normally walk to school.

3   The diagram represents a spinner.
The spinner is biased.

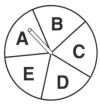

Michael spun the spinner 100 times and recorded the letter of
the section it stopped on each time. The results of his
experiment are recorded below:

Letter	A	B	C	D	E
Frequency	17	26	31	9	17

Jenny then spun the spinner 200 times and recorded the letter of the section it stopped on each time. The results of her experiment are recorded below:

Letter	A	B	C	D	E
Frequency	39	48	69	21	23

(a) Explain why the frequencies in Jenny's table of results are not double those in Michael's table of results, despite the fact that Jenny's number of spins was twice Michael's number of spins.

(b) Use the results to work out the best estimate of the probability of the spinner stopping on the sections marked
   (i) B **(ii)** D **(iii)** with a vowel
   when it is spun once.

4   The diagram represents a biased spinner. When it is spun once the probabilities of it stopping on each section are

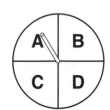

Section	A	B	C	D
Probability	0.32	0.22	0.17	0.29

The spinner is to be spun 1200 times.
Work out an estimate for the likely number of times it will stop on section C.

5   The diagram represents a spinner.
The spinner was spun 10 000 times and the faces it stopped on were recorded. The results are given below:

Face	A	B	C	D	E
No. of times	593	4009	1427	2003	1968

Explain clearly whether or not this information suggests that the spinner is biased.

9.2 Scatter graphs

Teaching reference:
pp 405–408, section 24.8

■ **Scatter graphs can be used to show whether two sets of data are related.**

■ **If the points on a scatter graph are very nearly along a straight line there is a high correlation between the variables.**

■ **Positive correlation: as one quantity increases the other one increases; as one quantity decreases the other one decreases.**

■ **Negative correlation: as one quantity increases the other quantity decreases.**

- No correlation: there *may* still be a relationship between the variables.

- A line which is drawn to pass as close as possible to all the plotted points on a scatter graph is called the *line of best fit*.

Example 3

The table shows the hours of sunshine and the rainfall, in mm, in 7 towns during last summer:

Sunshine (hours)	660	465	550	430	615	400	630
Rainfall (mm)	12	20	16	20	13	28	15

These values are plotted as points on the scatter graph below:

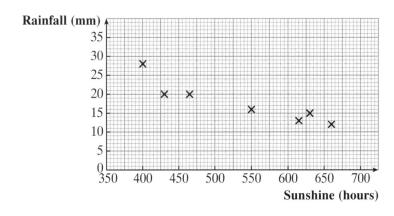

The hours of sunshine and rainfall in three other towns are shown in the next table:

Sunshine (hours)	Rainfall (mm)
380	32
525	25
620	21

(a) Plot these extra sets of values on the scatter graph.
(b) Describe the relationship between the hours of sunshine and the rainfall.
(c) Draw the line of best fit on the scatter graph.
(d) Use your line to find estimates of
    (i) the rainfall in a town with 500 sunshine hours,
    (ii) the number of hours of sunshine in a town with a rainfall figure of 18 mm.

(a) The complete scatter graph with the 3 extra points is

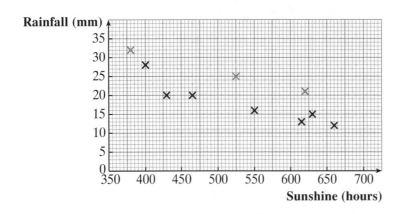

(b) The scatter graph shows that there is negative correlation.

(c) The line of best fit is as drawn here:

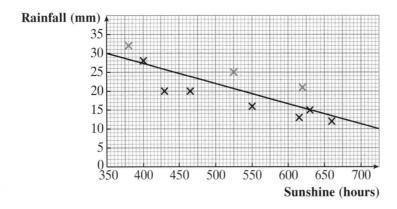

(d) The estimates from the line are
   (i) 500 hours gives a rainfall figure of 22 mm,
   (ii) 18 mm of rain gives a sunshine figure of 575 hours.

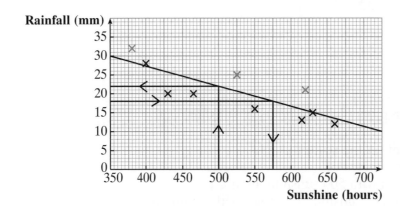

Exercise 9B

1   Jim sells second-hand cars.
    The table provides information about the value and mileage of
    8 cars on his forecourt:

Value (£)	6300	4200	8500	9500	2700	1850	3300	8200
Mileage	24 000	43 000	12 000	6500	94 000	101 000	51 000	14 000

   (a) Plot these values as points on a scatter graph.
   (b) Comment on the correlation between mileage and value.
   (c) Draw a line of best fit on the scatter graph.
   (d) Use your line of best fit to work out an estimate of
        (i)   the likely mileage for a car valued at £5000,
        (ii) the likely value of a car which has travelled
              72 000 miles.

2   Using one of the words

        positive   negative   zero

    describe the correlation shown in each of these scatter graphs:

   (a)

   (b)

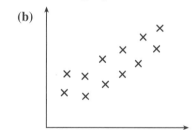

   (c)

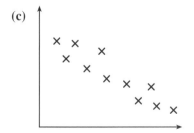

   (d)

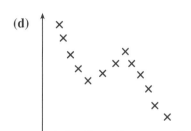

3   Give one example of a real-life situation where you would
    expect:
    (a) positive correlation
    (b) negative correlation.

4 Kieran has conducted a survey examining the heights and weights of some of the people in his village.

The results for six people are shown in the table below:

Height (cm)	Weight (kg)
178	80
157	57
182	81
155	53
148	42
175	74

These results are presented on the scatter diagram below:

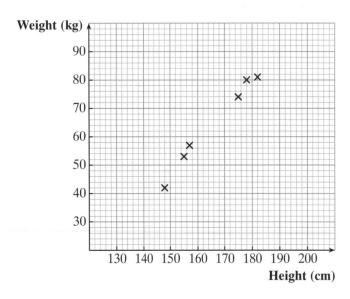

The results for a further four people are:

Height (cm)	192	138	163	180
Weight (kg)	88	36	60	79

(a) Plot these extra four values on the scatter diagram.
(b) Describe the relationship between the heights and weights of these ten people.
(c) Draw a line of best fit on your scatter diagram.
(d) Use your line of best fit to estimate:
    (i) the likely weight of a person of height 150 cm,
    (ii) the likely height of a person weighing 72 kg.

Summary of key points

■ You must write a probability as a fraction, a decimal or a percentage.

■ When one outcome prevents another outcome from happening, the outcomes are mutually exclusive.

■ The probabilities of all the possible mutually exclusive events (or outcomes) add up to 1.

■ In general, if A and B are mutually exclusive then $P(A \text{ or } B) = P(A) + P(B)$.

■ The calculated probability of an event happening
$$= \frac{\text{number of successful outcomes}}{\text{total number of possible outcomes}}$$

■ If the probability of an event happening is p then the probability of it not happening is $1 - p$.

■ If there are n mutually exclusive events all equally likely the probability of one event happening is $\frac{1}{n}$.

■ If there are n mutually exclusive events and a successful outcomes the probability of a successful outcome is $\frac{a}{n}$.

■ The estimated probability of an event in a game or experiment
$$= \frac{\text{number of successful trials}}{\text{total number of trials}}$$
and this is sometimes called the *relative frequency*.

■ The relative frequency, or estimated probability, becomes a better estimate as the total number of trials increases.

■ Scatter graphs can be used to show whether two sets of data are related.

■ If the points on a scatter graph are very nearly along a straight line there is a high correlation between the variables.

■ Positive correlation: as one quantity increases the other one increases; as one quantity decreases the other one decreases.

■ Negative correlation: as one quantity increases the other quantity decreases.

■ No correlation: there *may* still be a relationship between the variables.

■ A line which is drawn to pass as close as possible to all the plotted points on a scatter graph is called the *line of best fit*.

10 Handling data

10.1 Representing data

Teaching reference: pp 252, 391–404, sections 16.10, 24.1–24.7

- A pie chart is a way of displaying data that shows how something is shared or divided.
- A plot of values of a variable taken at regular intervals over a period of time is called a *time series*.
- Line graphs can be used to display continuous data.
- Histograms are usually used to display data that is grouped and continuous.
- Frequency polygons can show the general pattern of data represented by bar charts or histograms.
- A stem and leaf diagram retains the detail of the data and gives an idea of how the values are distributed.

Example 1

There are 240 students in Year 11 at Halley Court High School. As part of a survey Jason asked these students about their normal method of travelling to school. The responses are shown in the table below:

Method of travel	Frequency
Walk	80
Bus	96
Car	24
Cycle	40

Represent this information on a pie chart.

The fraction of students who walk is 80/240 = 1/3. For the pie chart, the fraction of the 360 degrees to represent the walkers is

$\qquad$ 1/3 of 360 = 120°

and for the other methods of travelling, the representative angles are

$\qquad$ bus: $\quad$ 96/240 of 360 = 144°
$\qquad$ car: $\quad$ 24/240 of 360 = 36°
$\qquad$ cycle: $\quad$ 40/240 of 360 = 60°

So the required pie chart is

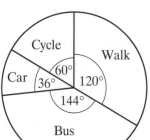

Example 2

The holiday brochure records the average maximum temperature in °C in Malta as follows:

Month	Temperature (°C)
April	17
May	21
June	26
July	29
Aug	30
Sept	27
Oct	23

Represent this information as a line graph.

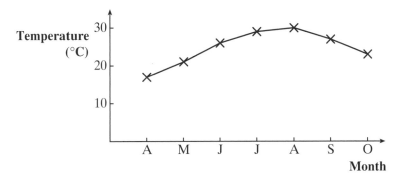

Example 3

As part of a project, Gemma has gathered information about the quarterly electricity bill at her home over a period of four years. The information is given in the table below:

Date of bill	Amount
Feb 1998	£255
May 1998	£204
Aug 1998	£112
Nov 1998	£156

Date of bill	Amount
Feb 1999	£263
May 1999	£210
Aug 1999	£117
Nov 1999	£160

Date of bill	Amount
Feb 2000	£270
May 2000	£212
Aug 2000	£120
Nov 2000	£172

Date of bill	Amount
Feb 2001	£294
May 2001	£223
Aug 2001	£128
Nov 2001	£185

Represent this information as a time series.

The graph for the time series will be as shown:

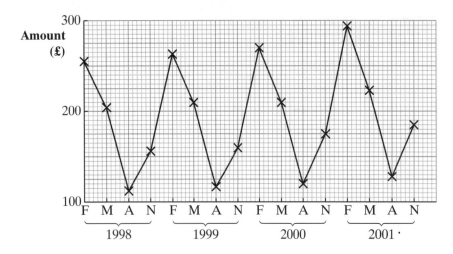

Example 4

The table shows information about the number of millimetres of rain that fell during the 52 weeks of a year:

Amount of rain (r) in mm	Frequency
$0 \leqslant r < 5$	8
$5 \leqslant r < 10$	6
$10 \leqslant r < 15$	17
$15 \leqslant r < 20$	10
$20 \leqslant r < 25$	7
$25 \leqslant r < 30$	4

Draw a frequency polygon for this frequency distribution.

Firstly we draw the histogram as ...   and mark the mid-points of the bars.

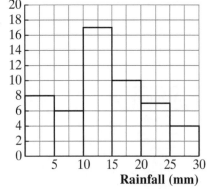

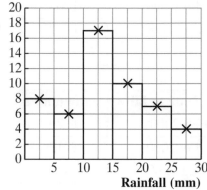

Now join the mid-points of the bars ...

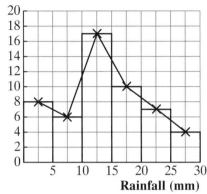

to give the frequency polygon below:

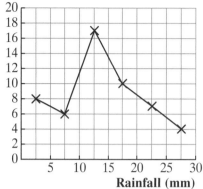

Example 5

The thirty students in Set 2 take a Science test marked out of 50.
Their marks are given below:

32	41	17	24	43	36	47	12	26	32
45	16	9	22	35	27	28	20	37	34
19	7	18	26	33	29	48	37	25	23

Using the tens as the stem, represent this information as a stem
and leaf diagram. Our key is 20/0 means $20 + 0$.

The stems are 0, 10, 20, 30 and 40; so the stem and leaf diagram is

0	7, 9
1	2, 6, 7, 8, 9
2	0, 2, 3, 4, 5, 6, 6, 7, 8, 9
3	2, 2, 3, 4, 5, 6, 7, 7
4	1, 3, 5, 7, 8

Example 6

The heights in cm of 30 students are recorded below.

> 170, 167, 172, 185, 159, 176, 186, 179, 168, 201,
> 164, 191, 182, 183, 169, 177, 173, 186, 183, 192,
> 149, 181, 171, 169, 173, 184, 188, 173, 179, 168.

Represent this data as a stem and leaf diagram. The stem will be
the first two digits followed by a zero.
The leaves will be the third digit.
So the stem and leaf diagram is:

140	9
150	9
160	4, 7, 8, 8, 9, 9
170	0, 1, 2, 3, 3, 3, 6, 7, 9, 9
180	1, 2, 3, 3, 4, 5, 6, 6, 8
190	1, 2
200	1

1   As part of a project, Fiona records the colour of hair of 40
people. Her results are as follows:

Hair colour	Frequency
Blonde	8
Brown	18
Ginger	3
Black	7
Grey	4

Represent this information on a pie chart.

2   Sumreen undertook a survey into the ages of people in a
supermarket. She recorded the ages of 60 people in the
supermarket as follows:

```
27  25  17  32   8  36  57  49  82  61  64  70  19  12  44
38  29  20  16  22  46  51  54  73  34  38  61  48  46  49
52  56  29  26  31  64  54  59  50  33  41  32  27  46  52
 6  15  46  42  38  48  53  52  45  39  33  42  40  61  56
```

Using the tens unit of the ages as the stem, represent this
information as a stem and leaf diagram.

3   The police recorded the speeds of 100 vehicles on a motorway.
The results are shown in the table below:

Speed (s) in mph	Frequency
$20 < s \leqslant 30$	8
$30 < s \leqslant 40$	12
$40 < s \leqslant 50$	19
$50 < s \leqslant 60$	22
$60 < s \leqslant 70$	30
$70 < s \leqslant 80$	6
$80 < s \leqslant 90$	3

Represent this information as a frequency polygon.

4   The table gives the mid-day temperature on the first ten days
in August one year:

Day	1	2	3	4	5	6	7	8	9	10
Temperature (°C)	23	23	26	22	28	32	29	30	26	32

Represent this information as a line graph.

5   The table shows information about Mrs Howe's gas bill, in £s,
     for the years from 1997 to 2001:

Year	1st quarter	2nd quarter	3rd quarter	4th quarter
1997	312	264	142	182
1998	325	271	150	190
1999	340	280	155	201
2000	346	288	172	218
2001	355	298	180	230

Represent this information graphically as a time series.

6   The costs, in £, of single rooms in 24 hotels are listed below.

110, 118, 125, 110, 134, 132, 169, 125,
127, 141, 110, 111, 120, 149,   99, 159,
120, 125, 127, 180, 163, 170, 109, 115.

Represent this information as a stem and leaf diagram.

7   Kate recorded the colour of the strips of the 24 teams in a
     league. Her results are represented in the frequency table.

Colour	Frequency
White	2
Red	8
Blue	5
Yellow	3
Green	2
Pink	4

Draw a pie chart for this information.

8   The table provides some information about the speeds, in
     mph, of some cars on a main road.

Speed (s) in mph	Frequency
$20 < s \leqslant 30$	8
$30 < s \leqslant 40$	12
$40 < s \leqslant 50$	16
$50 < s \leqslant 60$	14
$60 < s \leqslant 70$	10

Represent this information on a frequency polygon.

9 Thirty students took an examination. The maximum mark for the examination was 120. The marks obtained by the students were:

```
77  68  43  117  98   91  68   51  81  102
43  57  69   60  72  101  92  113  49   58
84  82  75   48  53   62  81   70  68   64
```

Represent this information as a stem and leaf diagram.

10 The monthly average mid-day temperatures in Nice are recorded in the table below:

Month	Temperature (°C)
October	23
November	18
December	16
January	15
February	15
March	17
April	20
May	22

Represent this information as a line graph.

11 Joseph works as a salesman. His quarterly sales figures, in £1000, for the years from 1997 to 2001 are given below:

	1997	1998	1999	2000	2001
Jan	110	115	118	123	130
April	152	158	162	167	174
July	252	260	263	268	273
Oct	207	210	215	221	229

Represent this information as a time series.

12 A bag contains 40 potatoes. The distribution of weights of the potatoes is given in the table below:

Weight (w) in g	Frequency
$0 < w \leqslant 100$	2
$100 < w \leqslant 200$	8
$200 < w \leqslant 300$	15
$300 < w \leqslant 400$	10
$400 < w \leqslant 500$	5

Represent this information as a frequency polygon.

13 There are 27 students in class 11Y. The frequency polygon for their weights is shown below:

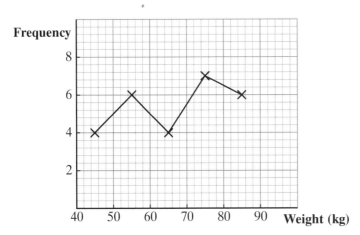

Represent this information as a frequency table.

14 The pie chart provides some information about the favourite colours of 120 students.
Use the pie chart to complete the frequency table:

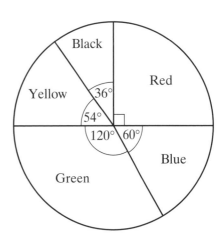

Colour	Frequency

15 Fifty people were asked to say how many miles they travelled to work. Their responses are given below:

```
 8  16  22  47  51   3  12   9  12  15
18  21  32  30  17  15  17   8   9   4
13  16  11  17  52  40  14  15  22  23
21   4  10  24  16  38  12  27  11  14
20   5   9  42  57  17   8   6  32   8
```

Represent this information as a stem and leaf diagram.

16 The quarterly figures in 1000s for the number of people visiting a holiday resort for the years 1998 to 2001 are given below:

Quarter	1998	1999	2000	2001
1st	112	113	102	124
2nd	206	204	185	223
3rd	517	510	470	540
4th	380	320	290	395

Represent this information as a time series.

10.2 Processing grouped data

Teaching reference: pp 239–266, sections 16.1–16.14

■ When data is arranged in ascending order of size
  ● the median is the middle value
  ● the lower quartile is the value one quarter of the way into the data
  ● the upper quartile is the value three quarters of the way into the data.

■ The interquartile range is the difference between the upper and lower quartiles:

  interquartile range = upper quartile − lower quartile

■ For a frequency distribution the mean can be worked out as

  $$\text{mean} = \frac{\Sigma fx}{\Sigma f}$$

  The sum of all the $(f \times x)$ values in the distribution
  The sum of all the frequencies

■ For grouped data
  ● you can state the class interval that contains the median
  ● you can calculate an estimate of the mean using the middle value of each class interval.

■ The cumulative frequency is the running total of the frequency up to the end of each class interval.

■ A box and whisker diagram turns the key features of a cumulative frequency distribution into a picture.

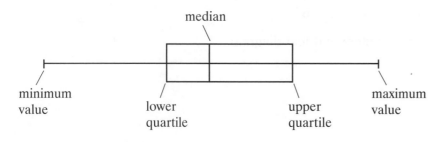

Example 7

The table provides information about the amount of rain that fell during the 52 weeks of one year:

Amount of rain (r) in mm	Number of weeks
$0 \leqslant r < 5$	8
$5 \leqslant r < 10$	6
$10 \leqslant r < 15$	17
$15 \leqslant r < 20$	10
$20 \leqslant r < 25$	7
$25 \leqslant r < 30$	4

Work out an estimate for the mean amount of rain that fell per week.

We set this out in tabular form:

Rainfall (x)	Mid-point of interval	Frequency (weeks)	$f \times x$
0 to <5	2.5	8	$8 \times 2.5 = 20$
5 to <10	7.5	6	$6 \times 7.5 = 45$
10 to <15	12.5	17	$17 \times 12.5 = 212.5$
15 to <20	17.5	10	$10 \times 17.5 = 175$
20 to <25	22.5	7	$7 \times 22.5 = 157.5$
25 to <30	27.5	4	$4 \times 27.5 = 110$
		Total sum of $f \times x$ or $\Sigma fx = 720$	

Adding these together gives this

So the estimate for the **total** amount of rain to fall during the 52 weeks is 720 mm.

So the mean rainfall per week is $\dfrac{720}{52} = 13.846$ mm

or 13.85 mm, correct to two decimal places.

Note: before you start this question you can see that the minimum amount of rain to fall each week is 0 mm and the maximum amount is 30 mm. So as a very, very rough guess you should be able to see that the mean amount is likely to be about halfway between 0 and 30, i.e. around 15 mm.

Example 8

The police recorded the speeds of 120 vehicles on a motorway.
The results are shown in the table below:

Speed (s) in mph	Frequency
$20 < s \leqslant 30$	9
$30 < s \leqslant 40$	15
$40 < s \leqslant 50$	24
$50 < s \leqslant 60$	25
$60 < s \leqslant 70$	36
$70 < s \leqslant 80$	7
$80 < s \leqslant 90$	4

(a) Construct a cumulative frequency table for this information.
(b) Draw a cumulative frequency diagram for the information.
(c) Use your cumulative frequency diagram to find an estimate for the median speed of the vehicles.
(d) Use your cumulative frequency diagram to work out an estimate for
   (i) the lower quartile of the speeds
   (ii) the upper quartile of the speeds
   (iii) the interquartile range of the speeds.
(e) Draw a box and whisker diagram for the data.

The Chief Constable decides to charge with a speeding offence all of the drivers of vehicles doing a speed of 77 mph or more.

(f) Using your cumulative frequency curve or otherwise, work out an estimate for the percentage of drivers likely to be charged with speeding.

(a) The cumulative frequency table is as shown:

Speed up to	Cumulative frequency	
30 mph	9	
40 mph	24	i.e. $9 + 15$
50 mph	48	i.e. $9 + 15 + 24$
60 mph	73	i.e. $48 + 25$
70 mph	109	i.e. $73 + 36$
80 mph	116	i.e. $109 + 7$
90 mph	120	i.e. $116 + 4$

Note: this should always be the sum of the frequency column.

(b) The cumulative frequency curve is

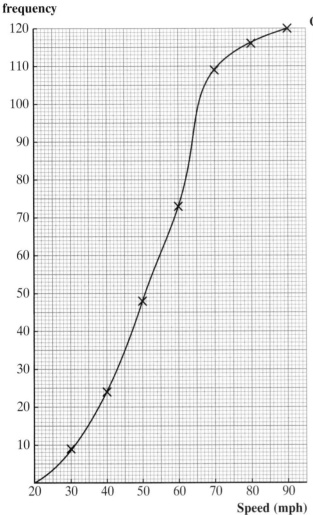

(c) The median speed is found by going half-way up the vertical axes and reading off the speed from the curve:

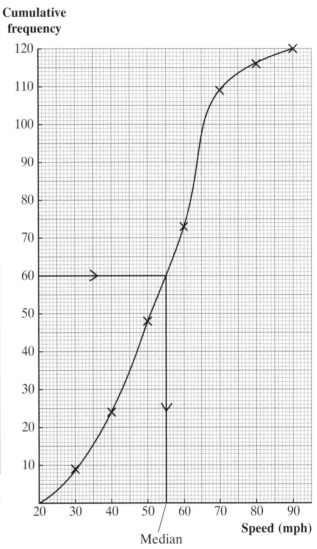

The median speed is approximately 55 mph.

(d) From the curve:

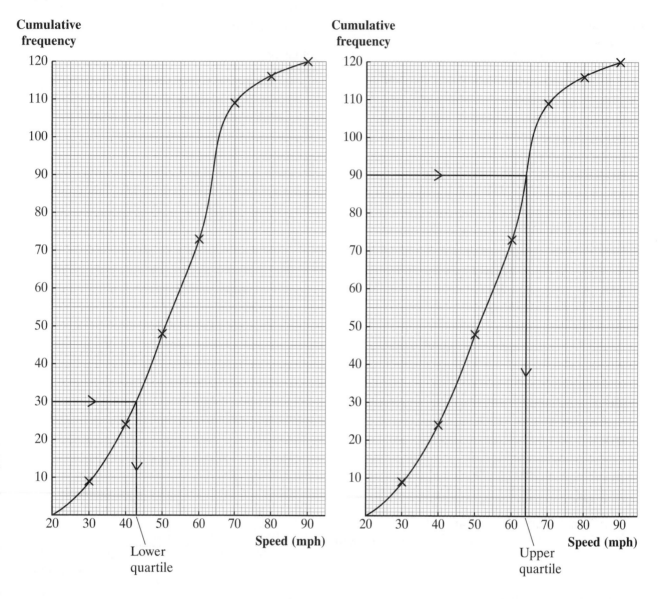

(i) The lower quartile speed is 43 mph.
(ii) The upper quartile speed is 64 mph.
(iii) So the interquartile range is

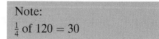

Note:
$\frac{1}{4}$ of $120 = 30$

$$\text{interquartile range} = \text{upper quartile} - \text{lower quartile}$$
$$= 64 - 43$$
$$= 21 \text{ mph}$$

(e) The box and whisker diagram for the data is

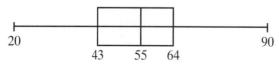

(f) The cumulative frequency curve indicates that there are

$$120 - 114 = 6 \text{ vehicles}$$

doing 77 mph or more.

That is 6 out of 120 = 6/120

$$= 1/20$$

or $\qquad = 5\%$

So the suggestion is that 5% of the drivers are likely to be charged with speeding.

> Note:
> Go up from a speed of
> 77 mph, then go across.

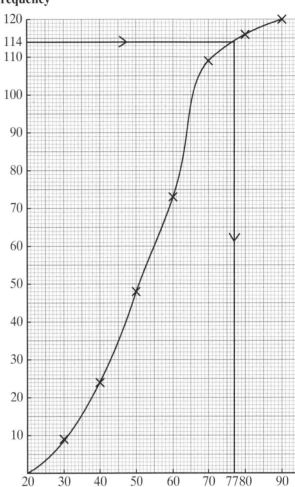

Cumulative frequency

Speed (mph)

Example 9

The diagram represents the histogram for a distribution.

Sketch, giving your reason, the cumulative frequency diagram for this distribution.

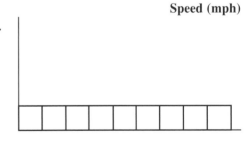

The cumulative frequencies will be created by building up steps like this:

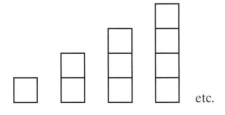

etc.

So the cumulative frequency diagram will be a straight line like this:

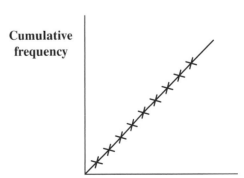

Cumulative frequency

Exercise 10B Links 16G, 16I, 16J, 16K, 16L, 16M

1 A bag contains 40 potatoes. The distribution of the weights of the potatoes is given in the frequency table below:

Weight (w) in g	Number of potatoes
$0 < w \leqslant 100$	3
$100 < w \leqslant 200$	7
$200 < w \leqslant 300$	17
$300 < w \leqslant 400$	11
$400 < w \leqslant 500$	2

Work out an estimate for the mean weight of the potatoes in the bag.

2 The grouped frequency table shows information about the number of hours worked by 200 doctors last week:

Number of hours (t) worked	Frequency
$10 < t \leqslant 20$	2
$20 < t \leqslant 30$	5
$30 < t \leqslant 40$	7
$40 < t \leqslant 50$	18
$50 < t \leqslant 60$	68
$60 < t \leqslant 70$	80
$70 < t \leqslant 80$	20

 (a) Work out an estimate for the mean number of hours worked by these doctors last week.
 (b) Draw a cumulative frequency diagram for this data.
 (c) Use your diagram to work out estimates for
  (i) the median
  (ii) the interquartile range for the number of hours.
 (d) Draw a box and whisker diagram for the data.

3 The median, upper quartile and lower quartile of a distribution are 48, 70 and 20 respectively.
The maximum value of the distribution is 100 and the minimum value is 0.
Draw the box and whisker diagram for this distribution.

4   The three diagrams labelled **(a)**, **(b)** and **(c)** represent the histograms for three different distributions:

(a)

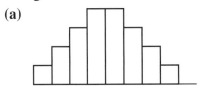

(b)

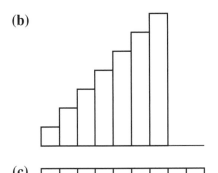

(c)

Sketch the cumulative frequency diagram in each of the three cases.

5   160 Year 11 students took an examination marked out of 100. The grouped frequency table shows information about their marks:

Mark (m)	Frequency
$0 < m \leqslant 10$	2
$10 < m \leqslant 20$	12
$20 < m \leqslant 30$	8
$20 < m \leqslant 40$	23
$40 < m \leqslant 50$	28
$50 < m \leqslant 60$	44
$60 < m \leqslant 70$	21
$70 < m \leqslant 80$	12
$80 < m \leqslant 90$	6
$90 < m \leqslant 100$	4

(a)   Work out an estimate of the mean mark of these 160 students.

(b)   Draw the cumulative frequency curve for this distribution.

(c)   Use the cumulative frequency curve to draw the box and whisker diagram for the distribution of marks.

The pass mark for the examination is 45.

Using the cumulative frequency curve, or otherwise, estimate the number of students who passed the examination.

6 The weights, in kg, of the 32 students in class 11B are represented by the stem and leaf diagram below:

3	2
4	3, 5, 8, 9
5	0, 1, 2, 2, 5, 6, 8
6	1, 1, 2, 2, 2, 4, 4, 7, 8, 8, 9
7	0, 0, 0, 2, 2, 8, 9
8	1, 5

(a) Use this information to work out
   (i) the median weight of the students
   (ii) the lower quartile of the weights
   (iii) the upper quartile of the weights.
(b) Draw a box plot of the weights of these students.

7 The box plot below is for the weights of some potatoes in a box.

Sketch a cumulative frequency curve for these weights.

8 The diagram below is the cumulative frequency curve for the marks scored by some students in an examination.
The maximum mark in the examination is 100.
(a) Use the curve to work out an estimate of
   (i) the median mark
   (ii) the interquartile range of the marks.
(b) Draw a box plot for the marks.
The pass mark for the examination was 42.
(c) Work out an estimate for the number of students who passed the examination.

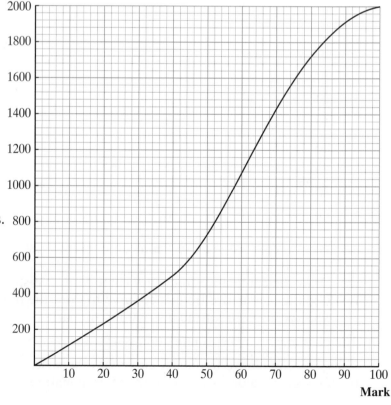

10.3 Interpreting data and results

■ When interpreting data or results, 'explain' does not mean 'describe'.

■ When interpreting data or results you must clearly state the statistics you are using to support your interpretation.

Example 10

The table provides information about the amount of rain that fell during 52 weeks of one year:

Amount of rain (r) in mm	Number of weeks
$0 \leqslant r < 5$	8
$5 \leqslant r < 10$	6
$10 \leqslant r < 15$	17
$15 \leqslant r < 20$	10
$20 \leqslant r < 25$	7
$25 \leqslant r < 30$	4

Wiqar works out an estimate for the mean amount of rain to fall per week that year.

He gives the answer of 120 mm.

Without calculating the estimated mean, **explain** how you know that Wiqar's answer must be wrong.

During the year, the amount of rain to fall weekly varies from 0 to 30 mm. So the mean must be somewhere between 0 and 30 mm, i.e. perhaps about 15 mm. Thus an answer of 120 mm is clearly wrong.

Example 11

Gary sells used cars. He has a number of cars on his forecourt. The values of the cars (£s) are plotted against the age (years) of the cars on a scatter diagram.
The results are shown below:

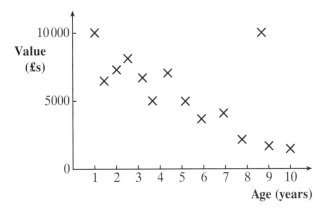

Comment on the relationship between age and value of the cars.

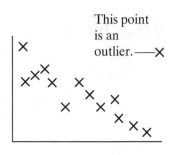

This point is an outlier.

The general trend of the scatter diagram is downwards. This means that, in general terms, as cars get older their value decreases.

However, as can be seen from the diagram, there is a point which is not in line with the general trend – it is an exception (such a point is usually called an **outlier**). This is an older car with a high value.

Example 12

The Year 11 students at Preble High School took a Geography examination.

Box and whisker diagrams were constructed for the distribution of marks for the girls and the boys.

These box and whisker diagrams are shown below:

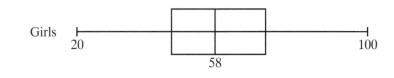

(a) Explain as fully as possible the conclusions that can be drawn from these diagrams.
(b) The Chair of Governors at the school states that, in general, the girls did better in the examination than the boys.

Explain whether this comment is valid or not.

(a) The box and whisker diagrams show
  - The range of marks for the girls was from 20 to 100, whilst for the boys it was from 0 to 100. So both genders had at least one person who scored full marks. But whilst the lowest score for the boys was zero, for the girls the lowest score was 20.
  - The median for the girls was 58, which is eight higher than the median for the boys.
  - The interquartile range for the boys was much greater than for the girls, suggesting that the boys' marks were far more spread out than the girls.

(b) The Chair of Governors is correct in thinking that the average (as measured by the median) mark for the girls is higher than that for the boys. But since the boys' marks are far more widely spread than those for the girls it is **not valid** to make any conclusion about whether girls did better than boys or vice versa. We really need further information to make such a comparison; information such as how many boys scored very high (or very low) marks, what proportion of boys scored a mark above the median for the girls, etc.

Example 13

The diagram below shows the line graphs for the average mid-day temperatures in England and Malta during the months from April to October one year:

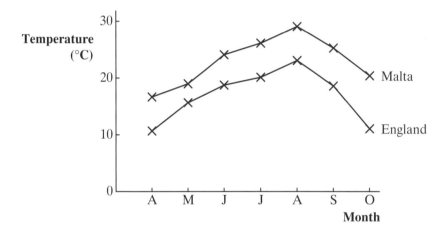

Write down three conclusions that can be made from these graphs.

Three conclusions are
(i)   The temperature in Malta is consistently higher than the temperature in England.
(ii) The month when the temperature difference between Malta and England is at its lowest is May.
(iii) The month when the temperature difference between Malta and England is at its greatest is October.

Exercise 10C   Links 29A

1   A group of girls and a similarly sized group of boys took a test. The average mark for the girls was higher than the average mark for the boys. Explain whether or not it is possible to conclude that, in general, the girls did better in the test than the boys.

2   The GCSE Mathematics results for the students at Lucea
High School and Jordan Hill County High School are
represented on the two cumulative frequency diagrams below:

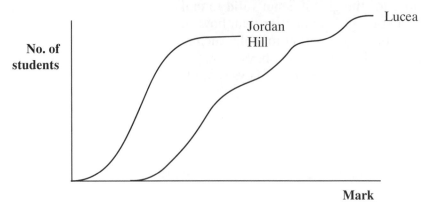

Comment as fully as possible on these results.

3   The number of hours worked each week and the pay received
by some of the workers at some different companies are shown
on the scatter diagram below:

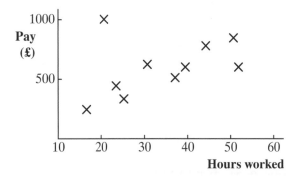

Comment on the relationship between hours worked per week
and pay.

4   The weights of some potatoes are shown in the grouped
frequency table below:

Weight (w) in g	Frequency
$0 < w \leqslant 100$	4
$100 < w \leqslant 200$	16
$200 < w \leqslant 300$	25
$300 < w \leqslant 400$	14
$400 < w \leqslant 500$	1

Samir works out an estimate for the mean weight of the
potatoes. He works out the answer to be 2840 g.

Without working out an estimate for the mean, explain why
Samir's answer must be incorrect.

5 Gary and Nick both sell second-hand cars.
Information about the values of the cars they have for sale is
shown on the two frequency polygons which have been drawn
on the same axes:

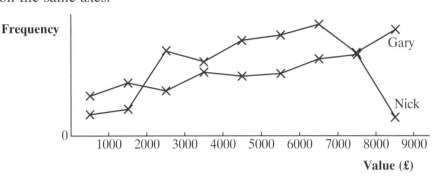

Make three valid comments comparing the values of the cars
Gary has for sale with those that Nick has for sale.

Summary of key points

- A pie chart is a way of displaying data that shows how
  something is shared or divided.

- A plot of values of a variable taken at regular intervals
  over a period of time is called a *time series*.

- Line graphs can be used to display continuous data.

- Histograms are usually used to display data that is
  grouped and continuous.

- Frequency polygons can show the general pattern of data
  represented by bar charts or histograms.

- A stem and leaf diagram retains the detail of the data and
  gives an idea of how the values are distributed.

- When data is arranged in ascending order of size
  - the median is the middle value
  - the lower quartile is the value one quarter of the way into
    the data
  - the upper quartile is the value three quarters of the way
    into the data.

- The interquartile range is the difference between the upper
  and lower quartiles:

  interquartile range = upper quartile − lower quartile

- For a frequency distribution the mean can be worked out as

  $$\text{mean} = \frac{\Sigma fx}{\Sigma f}$$ The sum of all the $(f \times x)$ values in the distribution

  The sum of all the frequencies

- For grouped data
  - you can state the class interval that contains the median
  - you can calculate an estimate of the mean using the middle value of each class interval.

- The cumulative frequency is the running total of the frequency up to the end of each class interval.

- A box and whisker diagram turns the key features of a cumulative frequency distribution into a picture.

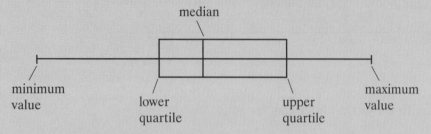

- When interpreting data or results, 'explain' does not mean 'describe'.

- When interpreting data or results you must clearly state the statistics you are using to support your interpretation.

Examination style practice paper

Section 1   **Answer ALL SIX questions.**
              You must not use a calculator.

1   (a)   Write 7639 correct to 1 significant figure.   (1)

   (b)   Work out an estimate for the value of $\dfrac{426 \times (32 + 26)}{7639}$. (2)

2   (a)   Work out the value of $5x - 3y$ when $x = 4$ and $y = -2$. (2)

   Alec has only five pound notes and ten pound notes in his wallet. He has f five pound notes and t ten pound notes. The total amount of money in his wallet is A pounds.

   (b)   Write down a formula for A in terms of f and t.   (2)

3

   Describe fully the single transformation which maps triangle **A** onto triangle **B**.   (3)

4   (a)   Solve the inequality $4x + 9 \geqslant 3$.   (2)
   (b)   Show the solution on a number line.   (1)

5   Here are the test scores of 14 students:

| 4   6   7   2   10   5   7 |
| 7   3   9   4   8   6   7 |

   Draw a box and whisker diagram to show this information. (3)

6   (a)   Write the number 0.007 in standard form.   (1)
   (b)   Divide 4×10^9 by 5×10^4. Give your answer in standard form.   (2)

Section 2   **Answer ALL SEVEN questions.**
              You may use a calculator.

1   There are nine marbles in a bag. One of the marbles is red. Three of the marbles are blue and the rest of the marbles are green. Heather picks one marble at random from the bag.

   Write down the probability that she will pick
         (a) a red marble   (b) a green marble.   (2)

2

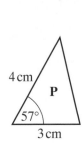 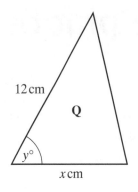

12 cm

4 cm

P

57°

3 cm

Q

$y°$

x cm

Diagram NOT accurately drawn.

Triangle **Q** is an enlargement of triangle **P**.

(a) Work out the scale factor of the enlargement. (1)
(b) Work out the value of x. (1)
(c) Write down the value of y. (1)

3 Mortar is a mixture of cement and sand.
40 kg of mortar contains 10 kg of cement.

Find the ratio of cement to sand in mortar.
Give your answer in the form $1 : n$. (2)

4 The diameter of a circle is 9 cm.
Work out the area of the circle.
Give your answer correct to 3 significant figures. (2)

5 Use your calculator to work out the value of $\dfrac{\sqrt{1.8^3}}{9.8 + 6.4^2}$.

Give your answer correct to 3 significant figures. (3)

6 (a) Expand and simplify $(x - 4)(x - 5)$. (2)
(b) Factorize $x^2 + 4x - 12$. (2)

7

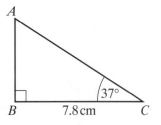

A

37°

B 7.8 cm C

Diagram NOT accurately drawn.

Triangle ABC is right-angled at B. $BC = 7.8$ cm.
Angle $ACB = 37°$.

Calculate the length of AB.
Give your answer correct to 3 significant figures. (3)

Answers

Exercise 1A

1 (i) (a) 2.3   (b) 4.9   (c) 8.5   (d) 6.4
     (e) 9.6   (f) 10.9   (g) 6.8   (h) 5.4
     (i) 11.2   (j) 20.1
   (ii) (a) 2.345   (b) 4.878   (c) 8.459   (d) 6.378
     (e) 9.644   (f) 10.924   (g) 6.825   (h) 5.355
     (i) 11.240   (j) 20.061

2 (a) 3.68   (b) 5.24   (c) 9.24   (d) 10.49
   (e) 8.70   (f) 12.44   (g) 15.69   (h) 20.35
   (i) 4.00   (j) 1.00

3 (a) 3.3   (b) 4.33   (c) 0.9   (d) 12.363
   (e) 6.06   (f) 5.00   (g) 0.1   (h) 6.8944
   (i) 16.00   (j) 0.01

Exercise 1B

1 (a) 46   (b) 440   (c) 3.7
   (d) 5500   (e) 0.0024   (f) 0.095

2 (a) 945   (b) 10 700   (c) 789 000
   (d) 0.835   (e) 0.002 38   (f) 0.0480

3 (a) 4900   (b) 80 000   (c) 380
   (d) 0.0289   (e) 2.60   (f) 5000

4 (a) 2800   (b) 5   (c) 18
   (d) 4   (e) 40   (f) 200 400
   (g) 0.12   (h) 75

Exercise 1C

1 16 egg boxes
2 4 cars
3 5 packs
4 £5.64
5 45 mph. Speedometer is only really accurate to within 5 mph
6 9.5 cm. Luisa will only be able to draw to the nearest millimetre
7 £3.33
8 £591.06
9 He will not be able to cut this accurately.
10 She will not be able to measure this accurately. The accuracy will depend on her weighing scales i.e. if they go up in intervals of 10 g she should aim for 130 g.

Exercise 1D

1 (a) 2:1   (b) 3:1   (c) 2:1
   (d) 2:1   (e) 2:1   (f) 3:2

2 (a) 1:2:3   (b) 4:2:1   (c) 5:3:2
   (d) 5:3:1   (e) 6:4:1   (f) 8:6:1

3 (a) 8:3   (b) 24:5   (c) 3:7
   (d) 11:24   (e) 16:25   (f) 7:20

4 (a) 8:3   (b) 4:1   (c) 12:1
   (d) 4:1   (e) 2:1   (f) 8:7

Exercise 1E

1 (a) $x = 1$ (b) $x = 4$ (c) $x = 2$
   (d) $x = 2$ (e) $x = 3$ (f) $x = 18$
   (g) $x = 12$ (h) $x = 40$

2 9 girls
3 28 cm
4 30 red sweets
5 9.6 cm
6 £216.80

Exercise 1F

1 (a) 15 and 10
   (b) 70 and 30
   (c) £24 and £6
   (d) £14.35 and £10.25
   (e) 200, 100 and 50
   (f) 90 cm, 30 cm and 30 cm
   (g) £120, £90 and £30
   (h) £20.50, £12.30 and £4.10

2 Juan gets £96, Gabrielle gets £64 and Kwame gets £40
3 800 women
4 $\frac{4}{7}$ **5** 17.5 cm   **6** 1:4   **7** 3:5

Exercise 1G

1 (a) 2.4   (b) 4.876   (c) 2.70   (d) 5.8   (e) 3.00
2 (a) 37   (b) 500   (c) 0.0075   (d) 96 300   (e) 489.30
3 12 bunches
4 £20.24, the bill must be for a whole number of pence.
5 Lucy cannot draw a side of length 3.33 cm; she cannot draw this accurately.
6 (a) 4:1   (b) 4:2:1   (c) 5:12
   (d) 4:5   (e) 6:1   (f) 5:8
7 (a) $x = 8$ (b) $x = 4$
8 5 cm
9 Pamela receives £70   **10** 3:2

Exercise 2A

1 (a) 64   (b) 9   (c) 108   (d) −16
   (e) 241   (f) 139   (g) −247   (h) 407

2 (a) 3   (b) −40   (c) −120   (d) 33
   (e) 25   (f) 4   (g) 41   (h) −102

3 (a) 8   (b) −2   (c) 4   (d) −4
   (e) 14   (f) 12   (g) 264   (h) −375

Exercise 2B

1 4.41   **2** 79.507   **3** −97.656 25
4 2.5   **5** 3.8   **6** 1.3
7 2.7   **8** 20.678 (3 d.p.)   **9** 3.75
10 81.92   **11** 15.376   **12** 3.24
13 6.456 (3 d.p.)   **14** 9.049 (3 d.p.)   **15** 12.634 (3 d.p.)

Exercise 2C

1 $x = 1.83$ **2** $x = 4.02$ **3** $x = 4.4$
4 $x = 9.9$ **5** $x = 3.11$ **6** $x = 2.81$

Exercise 2D

1 (a) 8×10^2 (b) 7×10^3 (c) 9×10^4
   (d) 8.72×10^2 (e) 9.2×10^3 (f) 8.7×10^3
   (g) 9.84×10^4 (h) 8.34×10^5 (i) 1.2×10^6

2 (a) 300   (b) 50 000   (c) 8 000 000
   (d) 25 000   (e) 3 800 000   (f) 23 600
   (g) 4 780 000   (h) 294 000   (i) 38 400 000

3 (a) 8×10^{-1} (b) 7.2×10^{-1} (c) 4×10^{-2}
   (d) 2×10^{-2} (e) 5.3×10^{-3} (f) 8.9×10^{-3}
   (g) 3.2×10^{-3} (h) 4.85×10^{-2} (i) 4.1×10^{-5}

4 (a) 0.2   (b) 0.03   (c) 0.0005
    (d) 0.021   (e) 0.000 034   (f) 0.000 58
    (g) 0.000 002 38   (h) 0.000 000 043 9   (i) 0.000 000 026 1
5 (a) 7.8×10^5 (b) 3.6×10^{-2}
    (c) 9.8×10^{10} (d) 5.7×10^{-6}
6 (a) 1.15×10^5 (b) 9.4×10^{-3}
    (c) 1.53×10^7 (d) 8.2×10^{-4}

Exercise 2E

1 (a) 103   (b) −42   (c) 48
    (d) 2   (e) $12\frac{1}{4}$ (f) 5
    (g) −248   (h) $8\frac{2}{3}$
2 (a) 19.683   (b) −14.44
    (c) 3.8   (d) 2.3
    (e) 5.51   (f) 14.784 (3 d.p.)
    (g) 4.745 (3 d.p.)
3 $x = 3.77$
4 $x = 9.25$
5 (a) 3×10^3 (b) 5.8×10^3 (c) 7.89×10^5
    (d) 8.63×10^4 (e) 5×10^{-1} (f) 6.1×10^{-2}
    (g) 2.1×10^{-4} (h) 3.81×10^{-4}
6 (a) 20 000   (b) 2300   (c) 384 000
    (d) 89 700 000   (e) 0.0003   (f) 0.000 002 1
    (g) 0.007 92   (h) 0.0826
7 (a) 5.6×10^{-2} (b) 3.9×10^7
8 (a) 8.04×10^4 (b) 1.528×10^{-4}

Exercise 3A

1

x	−3	−2	−1	0	1	2	3
y	−11	−8	−5	−2	1	4	7

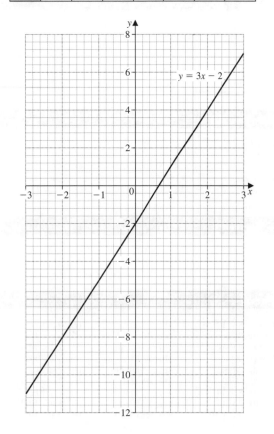

2

x	−3	−2	−1	0	1	2	3
y	9	7	5	3	1	−1	−3

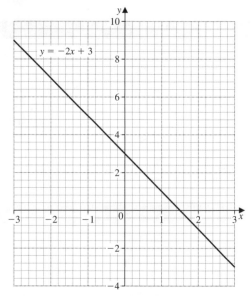

3

x	−6	−4	−2	0	2	4	6
y	−1	0	1	2	3	4	5

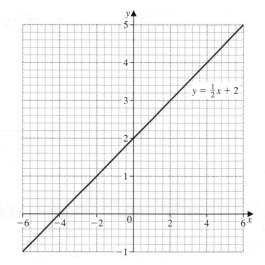

4

x	−2	−1	0	1	2	3	4	5	6
y	7	6	5	4	3	2	1	0	−1

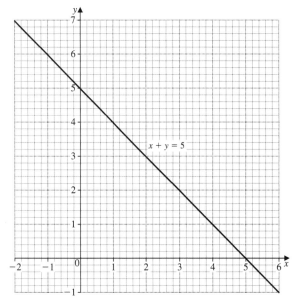

$x + y = 5$

6

x	−4	−2	0	2	4	6	8	10
y	5	4	3	2	1	0	−1	−2

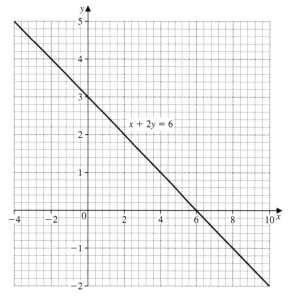

$x + 2y = 6$

5

x	−2	−1	0	1	2	3	4	5	6
y	−3	−2	−1	0	1	2	3	4	5

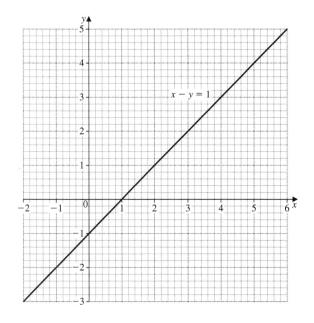

$x - y = 1$

7

x	−4	0	4	8	12
y	6	3	0	−3	−6

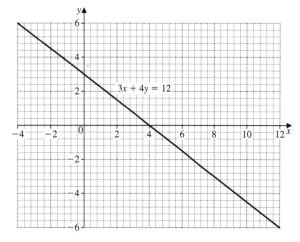

$3x + 4y = 12$

8

x	−3	0	3	6	9	12
y	−8	−6	−4	−2	0	2

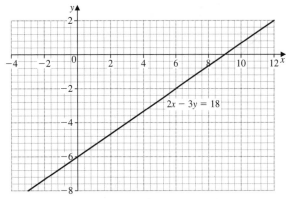

9

x	−8	−4	0	4	8
y	7	4	1	−2	−5

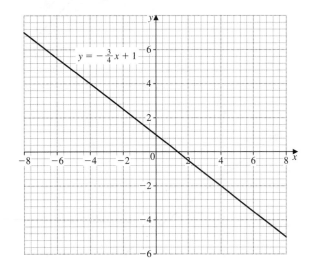

10 (a)

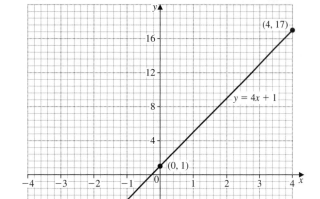

(b)

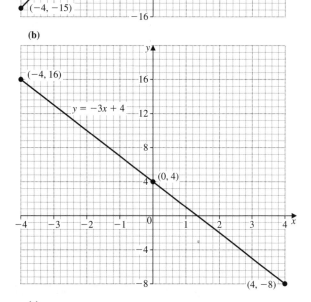

(c)

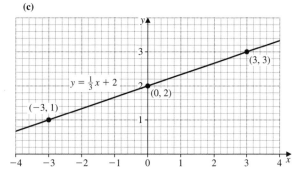

(d)

(e)

(f)

(g)

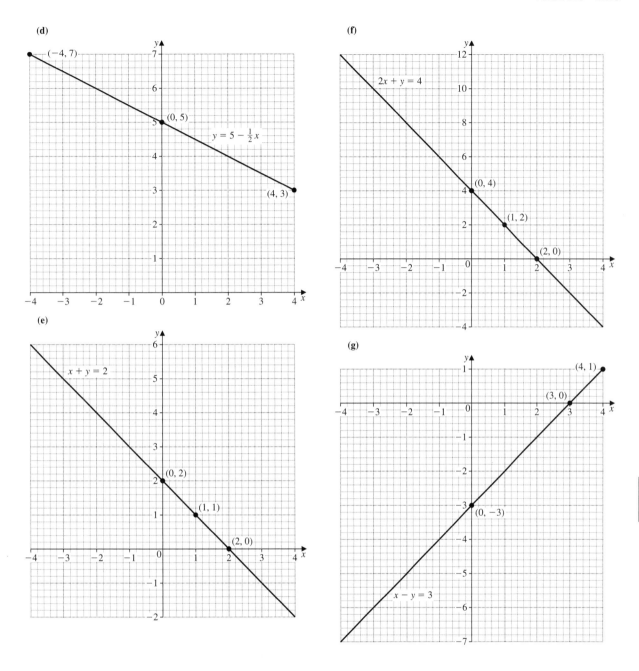

(h)

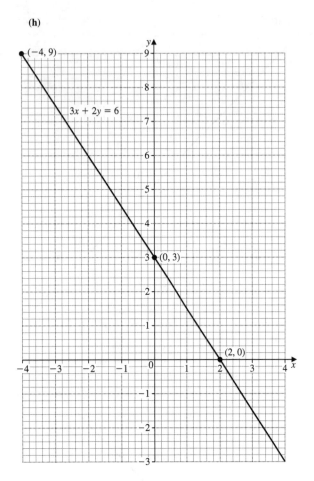

(i)

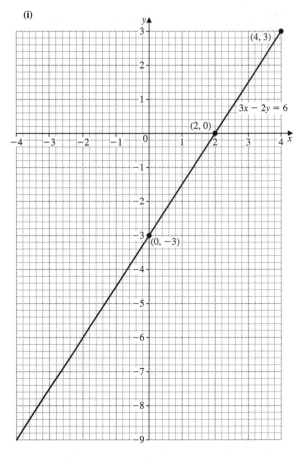

1 (a) 90 km   (b) 39 miles
2 (a) (i) 120 SF   (ii) 30 SF   (iii) 90 SF   (iv) 210 SF
   (b) (i) £42   (ii) £54   (iii) £87   (iv) £77

3 (a)

Kilograms (kg)	0	10	20	30	40	50
Pounds (lb)	0	22	44	66	88	110

(b)

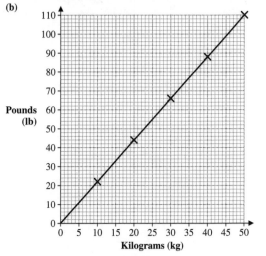

(c) (i) 73 lb   (ii) 19 kg

4 **(a)**

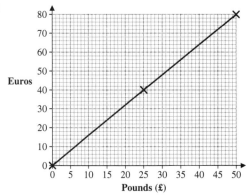

(b) **(i)** 70 Euros **(ii)** £23

5 **(a)**

Weight (lb)	Cooking time (min)
5	90
10	165
15	240
20	315

(b)

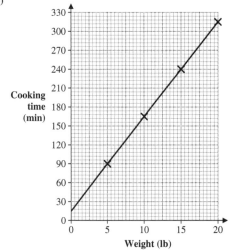

(c) **(i)** 270 min **(ii)** 11 lb

6 **(a)** 45 miles
(b) 11 : 00
(c) 30 min
(d) **(i)** 45 mph
(ii) 36 mph
(iii) 36 mph

7 **(a)**

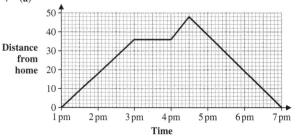

(b) 16 km per hour

8 **(a)** 24 m/s
(b) 12 s
(c) 432 m
(d) 3 s, 21.5 s

Exercise 3C

1 **(a)** The car was travelling at a constant speed and then slowed down steadily to travel at a slower speed.
(b) The car was travelling along, then suddenly stopped, stood at rest for a short while, then started moving again, speeding up suddenly to the speed it was originally travelling at.

2

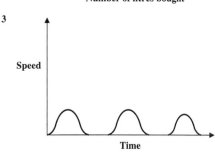

3

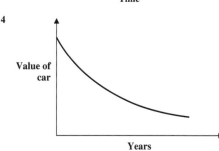

4

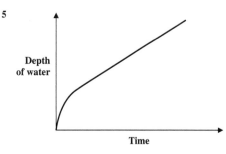

5

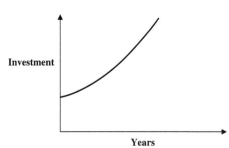

6

7

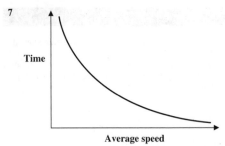

8 Derek earns a certain amount each week before overtime. He earns extra money in proportion to the number of overtime hours he works.

9 The runner starts from rest, slowly accelerating and reaching a constant running speed. She then slows down and stops, resting for about the same length of time that she ran for. She then suddenly starts running back to where she came from, but running at a slower speed, taking longer than on her outward run.

10 Pricing system is tiered so that at certain weight the price 'jumps' up.

Exercise 3D

1 (a)

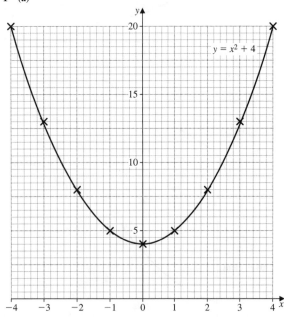

(b)

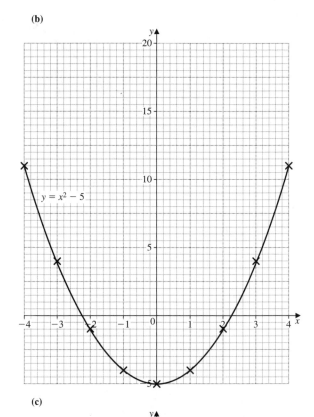

(c)

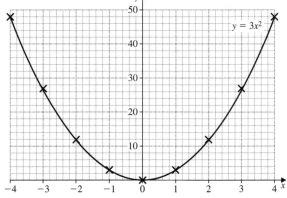

(d)

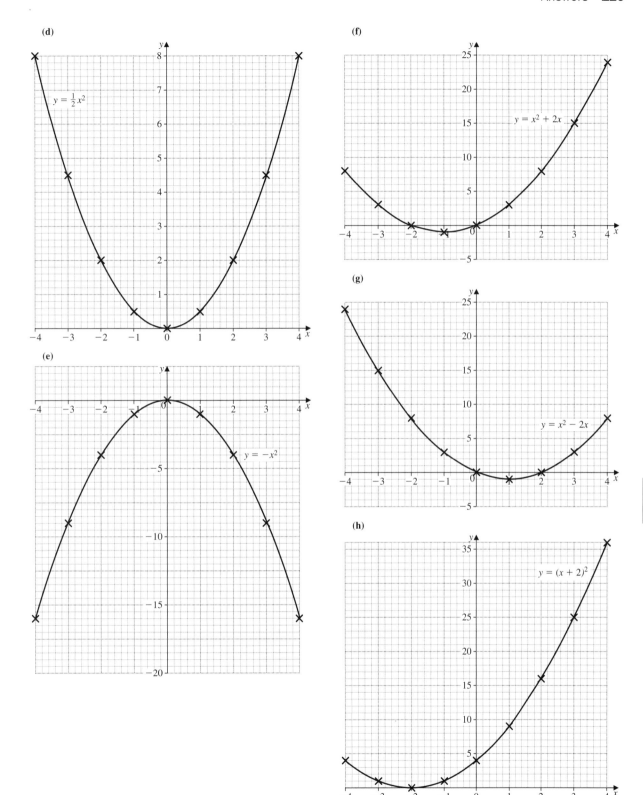

$y = \frac{1}{2}x^2$

(e)

$y = -x^2$

(f)

$y = x^2 + 2x$

(g)

$y = x^2 - 2x$

(h)

$y = (x + 2)^2$

(i)

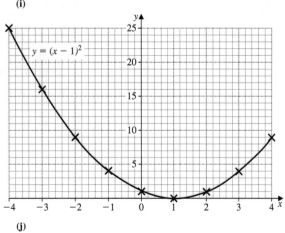

(j)

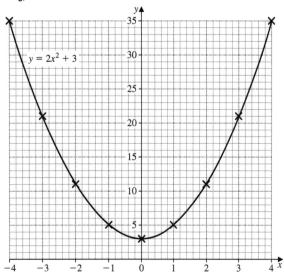

(k)

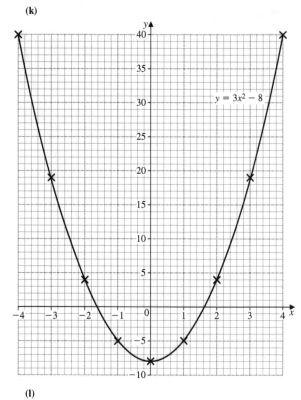

(l)

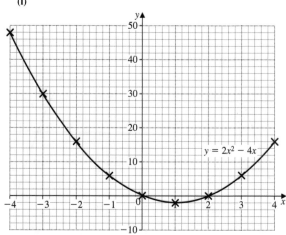

2 (a)

x	−4	−3	−2	−1	0	1	2
y	2	−1	−2	−1	2	7	14

(b)

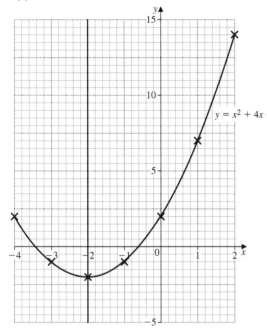

$y = x^2 + 4x + 2$

(c) $x = -2$

3 (a)

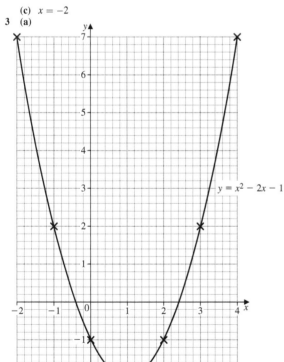

$y = x^2 - 2x - 1$

(b) Min. value of $y = -2$ and occurs at $x = 1$

4 (a)

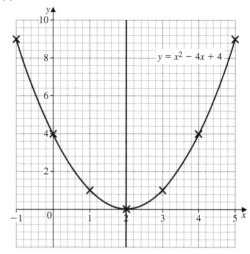

$y = x^2 - 4x + 4$

(b) $x = 2$

5 (a)

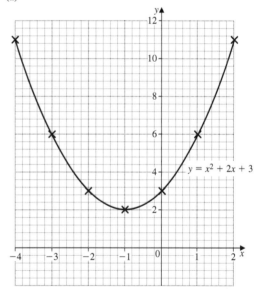

$y = x^2 + 2x + 3$

(b) Min. value of $y = 2$ and occurs at $x = -1$

6 (a)

x	-4	-3	-2	-1	0	1	2
y	11	1	-5	-7	-5	1	11

(b)

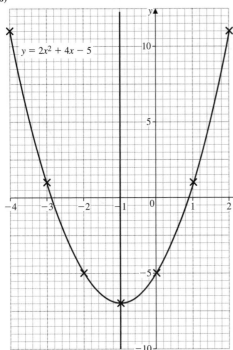

$y = 2x^2 + 4x - 5$

(c) $x = -1$
(d) Min. value of $y = -7$ and occurs at $x = -1$

7 (a)

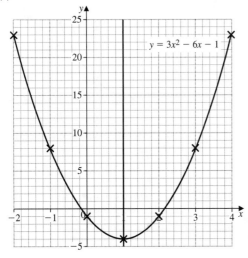

$y = 3x^2 - 6x - 1$

(b) $x = 1$
(c) Min. value of $y = -4$ and occurs at $x = 1$

8 (a)

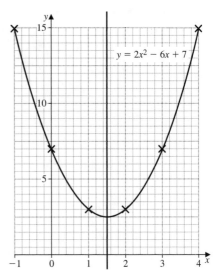

$y = 2x^2 - 6x + 7$

(b) $x = 1\frac{1}{2}$

9 (a)

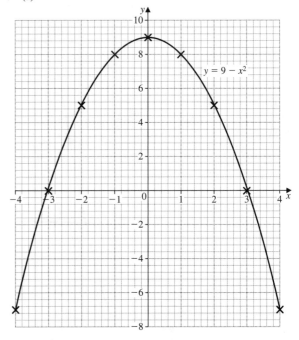

$y = 9 - x^2$

(b)

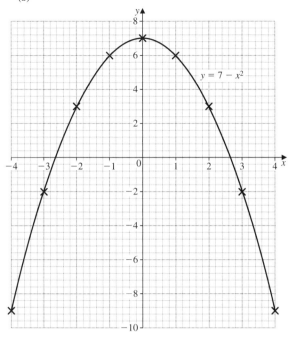

$y = 7 - x^2$

(c)

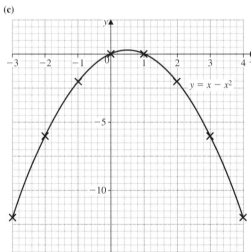

$y = x - x^2$

(d)

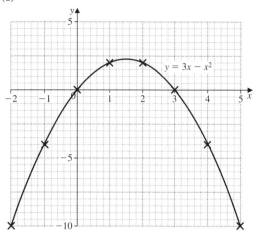

$y = 3x - x^2$

10 (a)

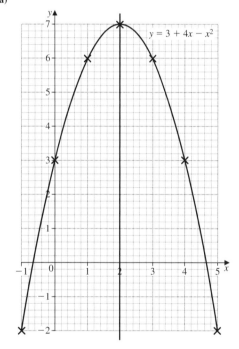

$y = 3 + 4x - x^2$

(b) $x = 2$

(c) Max. value of $y = 7$ and occurs at x=2

Exercise 3E

1

x	−3	−2	−1	0	1	2	3
y	−7	−3	1	5	9	13	17

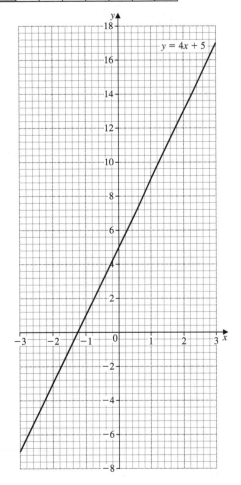

$y = 4x + 5$

2

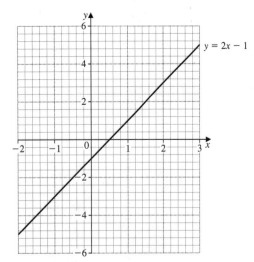

$y = 2x - 1$

3 (a)

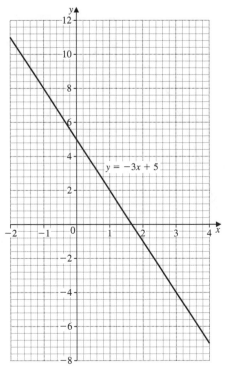

$y = -3x + 5$

(b) Another way of writing $y = -3x + 5$ is $3x + y = 5$

4

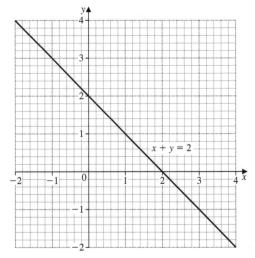

$x + y = 2$

5

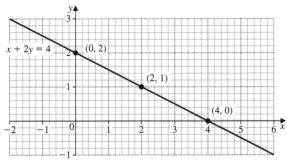

$x + 2y = 4$

(0, 2)

(2, 1)

(4, 0)

6

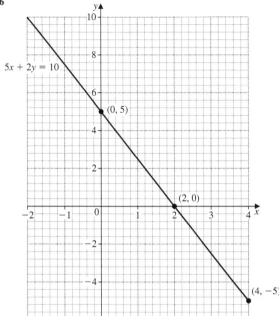

$5x + 2y = 10$

(0, 5)

(2, 0)

(4, −5)

7 **(a)** **(i)** 90 litres **(ii)** 80 litres **(iii)** 125 litres
   (b) **(i)** 11 gallons **(ii)** $35\frac{1}{2}$ gallons **(iii)** $24\frac{1}{2}$ gallons
8 **(a)** 70 miles
   (b) 42 minutes
   (c) 70 mph
   (d) 10 : 30
   (e) 60 mph

9

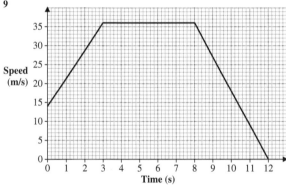

10 Kate starts to fill the bath at a steady rate, and whilst she is filling it the water remains at a constant temperature. She then stops filling the bath and the water cools down, at a steady rate. Kate then tops the bath up quickly and the temperature rises quickly. She then stops filling the bath and again the water cools steadily. Then Kate lets the water out of the bath, the water continuing to cool whilst she does so.

11

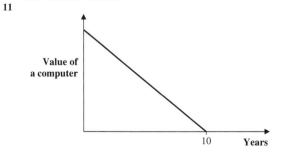

12 **(a)**

x	−3	−2	−1	0	1	2	3
y	1	−2	−3	−2	1	6	13

(b) (c)

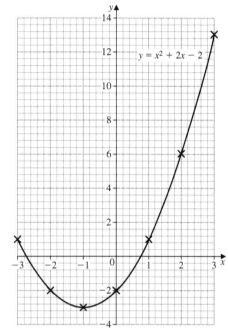

$y = x^2 + 2x - 2$

line of symmetry is $x = -1$
(d) $x = -2.7$ and $x = 0.7$

13 **(a)**

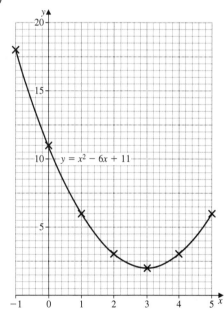

$y = x^2 - 6x + 11$

(b) Min. value of $y = 2$ and occurs at $x = 3$

14 (a)

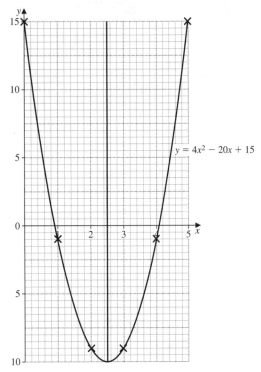

(b) $x = 2\frac{1}{2}$

15 (a)

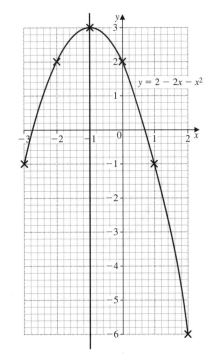

(b) $x = -1$
(c) Max. value of $y = 3$; occurs at $x = -1$

Exercise 4A

1 (a) $a^2 + 9a + 18$ (b) $b^2 + 6b + 5$ (c) $c^2 + 10c + 16$
 (d) $d^2 + 7d + 12$ (e) $e^2 + 13e + 36$ (f) $f^2 + 12f + 35$
2 (a) $ab + 5a + 4b + 20$ (b) $cd - 2c + 6d - 12$
 (c) $pq - 4p - q + 4$ (d) $xy + 3x - 8y - 24$
 (e) $at - a - 9t + 9$ (f) $bc - 7b + 3c - 21$
3 (a) $a^2 + 3a - 4$ (b) $b^2 - 3b - 18$ (c) $c^2 - 9c + 14$
 (d) $d^2 - 16$ (e) $e^2 - 12e + 27$ (f) $f^2 + 2f - 24$
 (g) $g^2 - 3g - 40$ (h) $x^2 - 36$ (i) $y^2 + 7y - 18$
4 (a) $3a^2 - 5a - 2$ (b) $6b^2 - 7b - 20$
 (c) $8c^2 - 34c + 21$ (d) $2cd + 4c - 3d - 6$
 (e) $10e^2 - 51e + 27$ (f) $10ef - 15e + 8f - 12$
 (g) $9g^2 - 25$ (h) $12x^2 + 35x + 8$
 (i) $16y^2 - 81$ (j) $6a^2 - ab - 2b^2$
 (k) $8ac - 20ad + 6bc - 15bd$ (l) $14x^2 - 41xy + 15y^2$
 (m) $49p^2 - 4q^2$
5 (a) $a^2 + 10a + 25$ (b) $b^2 - 2b + 1$
 (c) $c^2 + 16c + 36$ (d) $d^2 - 14d + 49$
 (e) $4e^2 + 12e + 9$ (f) $9f^2 - 24f + 16$
 (g) $25g^2 + 10g + 1$ (h) $49h^2 - 28h + 4$
 (i) $a^2 + 2ab + b^2$ (j) $9x^2 - 6xy + y^2$
 (k) $9m^2 + 30mn + 25n^2$ (l) $16p^2 - 56pq + 49q^2$
6 (a) $a^2 + 4a + 2$ (b) $4b^2 + 6b - 5$
 (c) $2c^2 - 6c - 2$ (d) $2d^2 + 2d + 25$
 (e) $30e + 25$ (f) $8f$

Exercise 4B

1 (a) $a(2a + 3)$ (b) $3(2b^2 - 3)$ (c) $c(c - 5)$
 (d) $5(2d^2 + 1)$ (e) $a(x^2 - 3)$ (f) $x(bx + 2)$
 (g) $y(5y - c)$ (h) $t(at + b)$ (i) $2(4a^2 - 3b)$
 (j) $a(b^2 + c)$ (k) $3(ax^2 - 2bc)$ (l) $t(7 - 10t)$
2 (a) $3a(a + 2)$ (b) $3b(2b - 3)$ (c) $5c(3c - 1)$
 (d) $5d(2d + 3)$ (e) $ax(x - 3)$ (f) $4x(x + 2b)$
 (g) $cy(y - 3)$ (h) $at(t + 1)$ (i) $ab(a + b)$
 (j) $4y(3xy - 2)$ (k) $3a(2a + 3b)$ (l) $ab(3ab - 4)$
 (m) $3pq(2p + 3)$ (n) $2cd(4d - 3c)$ (o) $2bx(2x + 1)$
 (p) $3t^2(c - 2)$ (q) $ax^2(7 + 3b)$ (r) $bn^2(5 + a)$
3 (a) $(x + 1)(x + 2)$ (b) $(x - 2)(x + 1)$ (c) $(x - 3)(x - 1)$
 (d) $(x - 1)(x + 7)$ (e) $(x - 7)(x - 1)$ (f) $(x + 1)(x + 7)$
 (g) $(x + 1)^2$ (h) $(x - 5)(x + 1)$ (i) $(x - 1)^2$
 (j) $(x - 4)(x - 1)$ (k) $(x - 2)^2$ (l) $(x - 4)(x + 2)$
 (m) $(x - 8)(x - 1)$ (n) $(x + 3)^2$ (o) $(x - 2)(x + 5)$
 (p) $(x - 4)^2$ (q) $(x - 6)(x + 2)$ (r) $(x - 1)(x + 12)$
 (s) $(x - 5)(x + 3)$ (t) $(x - 7)(x - 2)$ (u) $(x - 4)(x + 5)$
 (v) $(x - 6)(x - 3)$ (w) $(x + 5)^2$ (x) $(x - 6)(x + 4)$

Exercise 4C

1 $d = \dfrac{P}{5}$ **2** $I = \dfrac{P}{V}$ **3** $B = \dfrac{A}{L}$

4 $d = \dfrac{C}{\pi}$ **5** $h = \dfrac{V}{lb}$ **6** $r = \dfrac{A}{\pi l}$

7 $x = \dfrac{y + 3}{4}$ **8** $n = \dfrac{t - 5}{3}$ **9** $y = P - 2x$

10 $x = \dfrac{P - y}{2}$ **11** $m = \dfrac{y - c}{x}$ **12** $u = v + gt$

13 $t = \dfrac{u - v}{g}$ **14** $b = \dfrac{2A}{h}$ **15** $a = 2s - b - c$

16 $T = \dfrac{100I}{PR}$ **17** $D = TV$ **18** $V = \dfrac{D}{T}$

19 $V = \dfrac{kT}{P}$ **20** $T = \dfrac{PV}{k}$ **21** $v = \dfrac{I}{m} + u$

22 $h = \dfrac{2A}{a + b}$ **23** $b = \dfrac{2A}{h} - a$ **24** $x = 3(y + 2)$

25 $x = \frac{1}{2}y + 1$ **26** $y = \frac{1}{3}x - 2$ **27** $A = 2(17 - H)$

28 $x = 5 - 2y$ **29** $x = \dfrac{2y + 6}{3}$ **30** $y = \dfrac{3x - 6}{2}$

Exercise 4D

1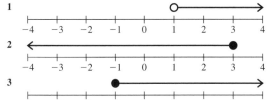

2

3

4

5

6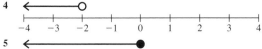

7

8

9

10

11

12

13 $x \leqslant -1$
14 $x > 3$
15 $0 \leqslant x < 2$
16 $-3 < x < 3$
17 $-2 < x \leqslant 0$
18 $-1 \leqslant x \leqslant 3$
19 (a) $-3, -2, -1, 0$

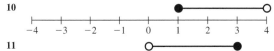

(b) $1, 2, 3$

(c) $-2, -1, 0, 1, 2, 3, 4$

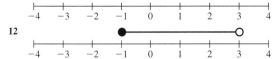

(d) $-3, -2$

(e) $-1, 0, 1, 2, 3$

(f) $-2, -1, 0$

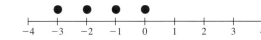

20 (a) $2, 3, 4$

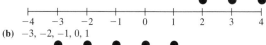

(b) $-3, -2, -1, 0, 1$

(c) $1, 2, 3$

(d) $0, 1, 2$

(e) $0, 1, 2$

(f) $-4, -3, -2, -1$

Exercise 4E

1 $x < 4$	**2** $x \geqslant 6$	**3** $x \leqslant 6$
4 $x > 6$	**5** $x < 9$	**6** $x > 4$
7 $x \geqslant 0$	**8** $x \leqslant 5$	**9** $x \geqslant 3$
10 $x < 2$	**11** $x > 3$	**12** $x \geqslant 1$

13 $x > 2\frac{3}{4}$

14 $x \leqslant \frac{1}{2}$

15 $x \geqslant -2$

16 $x > \frac{5}{4}$

17 $x < -1\frac{1}{2}$

18 $x \leqslant \frac{3}{4}$

19 $2, 3, 4$

20 $-3, -2, -1, 0, 1$

21 $-2, -1, 0, 1$

22 $0, 1, 2, 3$

23 −3, −2, −1, 0

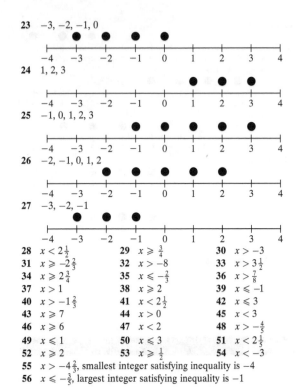

24 1, 2, 3

25 −1, 0, 1, 2, 3

26 −2, −1, 0, 1, 2

27 −3, −2, −1

28 $x < 2\frac{1}{2}$ **29** $x \geqslant \frac{3}{4}$ **30** $x > -3$
31 $x \geqslant -2\frac{2}{3}$ **32** $x > -8$ **33** $x > 3\frac{1}{2}$
34 $x \geqslant 2\frac{3}{4}$ **35** $x \leqslant -\frac{2}{3}$ **36** $x > \frac{7}{8}$
37 $x > 1$ **38** $x \geqslant 2$ **39** $x \leqslant -1$
40 $x > -1\frac{2}{3}$ **41** $x < 2\frac{1}{2}$ **42** $x \leqslant 3$
43 $x \geqslant 7$ **44** $x > 0$ **45** $x < 3$
46 $x \geqslant 6$ **47** $x < 2$ **48** $x > -\frac{4}{5}$
49 $x \leqslant 1$ **50** $x \leqslant 3$ **51** $x < 2\frac{1}{5}$
52 $x \geqslant 2$ **53** $x \geqslant \frac{1}{2}$ **54** $x < -3$
55 $x > -4\frac{2}{3}$, smallest integer satisfying inequality is −4
56 $x \leqslant -\frac{3}{5}$, largest integer satisfying inequality is −1

Exercise 4F

1 (a) $a^2 + 8a + 15$ (b) $b^2 + 2b - 8$
(c) $ab + 3a + 7b + 21$ (d) $c^2 - 11c + 30$
(e) $cd + 8c - d - 8$ (f) $d^2 - 25$
(g) $e^2 - 4e - 12$ (h) $f^2 + 6f + 9$
(i) $g^2 - 49$ (j) $tu - t + 9u - 9$
(k) $u^2 - 64$ (l) $v^2 - 12v + 36$

2 (a) $4a^2 + 17a - 15$ (b) $4b^2 + 15b - 4$
(c) $12c^2 + 19c + 5$ (d) $16bc + 8b - 6c - 3$
(e) $4d^2 - 49$ (f) $36e^2 - 60e + 25$
(g) $6f^2 - 19f + 8$ (h) $28ef - 8e + 35f - 10$
(i) $64g^2 - 1$ (j) $9h^2 + 24h + 16$
(k) $24j^2 + 7j - 6$ (l) $12k^2 + 44k + 35$
(m) $12m^2 - 17mn - 5n^2$ (n) $12x^2 + 13xy - 14y^2$
(o) $9p^2 - 16q^2$ (p) $25t^2 - 40tu + 16u^2$

3 (a) $a(7a + 5)$ (b) $4(2b^2 - 3)$ (c) $c(9c + a)$
(d) $5(3a^2 - 2b)$ (e) $b(a^2 + 3)$ (f) $d(d - 1)$

4 (a) $3a(4a - 3)$ (b) $ab(b - 7)$ (c) $5a(3b^2 + 4)$
(d) $2c(3c + 1)$ (e) $pq(3q - 2)$ (f) $6xy(4y + 3x)$

5 (a) $(x + 1)(x + 5)$ (b) $(x - 1)(x + 2)$ (c) $(x - 4)(x - 3)$
(d) $(x + 10)^2$ (e) $(x - 9)(x + 2)$ (f) $(x - 6)^2$

6 (a) $a = \dfrac{P}{m}$ (b) $h = \dfrac{E}{mg}$ (c) $x = \dfrac{TL}{k}$

(d) $L = \dfrac{kx}{T}$ (e) $r = \dfrac{V - e}{I}$ (f) $L = \dfrac{l}{1 + at}$

(g) $t = \dfrac{l - L}{aL}$ (h) $n = \dfrac{2S}{a + l}$ (i) $l = \dfrac{2S}{n} - a$

7 (a)

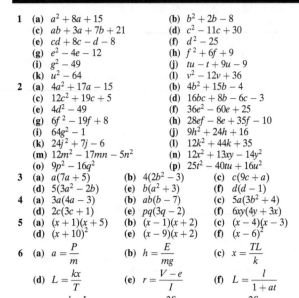

(b)

(c)

8 (a) $x \geqslant 1$ (b) $x < -1$ (c) $-3 < x \leqslant 2$
(d) $-3 \leqslant x \leqslant 3$ (e) $-4 \leqslant x < 0$

9 (a) −2, −1, 0, 1

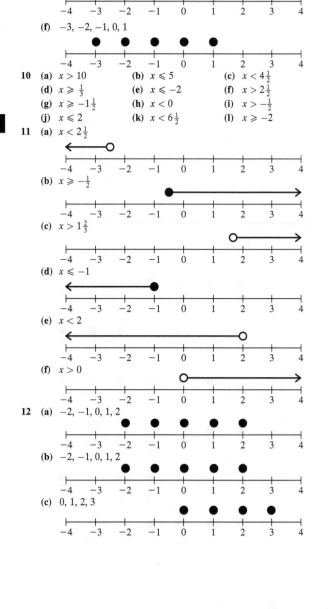

(b) 0, 1, 2, 3

(c) −2, −1, 0, 1, 2, 3

(d) −2, −1, 0, 1, 2

(e) −1, 0, 1, 2, 3, 4

(f) −3, −2, −1, 0, 1

10 (a) $x > 10$ (b) $x \leqslant 5$ (c) $x < 4\frac{1}{2}$
(d) $x \geqslant \frac{1}{3}$ (e) $x \leqslant -2$ (f) $x > 2\frac{1}{2}$
(g) $x \geqslant -1\frac{1}{2}$ (h) $x < 0$ (i) $x > -\frac{1}{2}$
(j) $x \leqslant 2$ (k) $x < 6\frac{1}{2}$ (l) $x \geqslant -2$

11 (a) $x < 2\frac{1}{2}$

(b) $x \geqslant -\frac{1}{2}$

(c) $x > 1\frac{2}{3}$

(d) $x \leqslant -1$

(e) $x < 2$

(f) $x > 0$

12 (a) −2, −1, 0, 1, 2

(b) −2, −1, 0, 1, 2

(c) 0, 1, 2, 3

Exercise 5A

1 (a) $a = 5$ cm
  (b) $b = 30$ cm
  (c) $c = 16.16$ cm (2 d.p.)
  (d) $d = 7.16$ cm (2 d.p.)
2 (a) $a = 7.19$ cm (2 d.p.)
  (b) $b = 3.76$ cm (2 d.p.)
  (c) $c = 16.83$ cm (2 d.p.)
  (d) $d = 19.68$ cm (2 d.p.)
3 Length of diagonal = 28.30 cm (2 d.p.)
4 Length of cable = 50.99 m (2 d.p.)
5 $AD = 10.44$ cm (2 d.p.)

Exercise 5B

1 (a) 12 cm
  (b) 16 cm
  (c) 18.73 cm (2 d.p.)
  (d) 11.73 cm (2 d.p.)
2 (a) $a = 5.02$ cm (3 s.f.)
  (b) $b = 10.7$ cm (3 s.f.)
  (c) $c = 8.65$ cm (3 s.f.)
  (d) $d = 19.4$ cm (3 s.f.)
3 (a) Height = 13.4 cm (3 s.f.)
  (b) Height = 11.0 cm (3 s.f.)
4 Length of side = 8.49 cm (3 s.f.)
5 Ladder reaches 7.75 m up the wall (3 s.f.)
6 Distance from edge of ramp to building = 1.98 m (3 s.f.)

Exercise 5C

1 (a) 5.14 (3 s.f.)
  (b) 0.141 (3 s.f.)
  (c) 1.25 (3 s.f.)
  (d) 0.557 (3 s.f.)
2 (a) $60.945°$ (3 d.p.)
  (b) $29.683°$ (3 d.p.)
  (c) $77.444°$ (3 d.p.)
  (d) $68.962°$ (3 d.p.)
  (e) $80.823°$ (3 d.p.)
  (f) $36.870°$ (3 d.p.)
3 (a) $a = 33.7°$ (3 s.f.)
  (b) $b = 72.6°$ (3 s.f.)
  (c) $c = 54.2°$ (3 s.f.)
  (d) $d = 50.1°$ (3 s.f.)
  (e) $e = 67.4°$ (3 s.f.)
  (f) $f = 59.4°$ (3 s.f.)
4 (a) $a = 10.62°$ (2 d.p.)
  (b) Bearing of Hitchin from Bedford = 169.38° (2 d.p.)
5 (a) $a = 9.60$ cm (3 s.f.)
  (b) $b = 10.1$ cm (3 s.f.)
  (c) $c = 7.85$ cm (3 s.f.)
  (d) $d = 21.6$ cm (3 s.f.)
  (e) $e = 13.0$ cm (3 s.f.)
  (f) $f = 5.04$ cm (3 s.f.)
6 Height ladder reaches up wall = 5.23 m (3 s.f.)
7 Length = 21.4 cm (3 s.f.)

Exercise 5D

1 (a) $a = 48.6°$ (3 s.f.)
  (b) $b = 41.8°$ (3 s.f.)
  (c) $c = 48.7°$ (3 s.f.)
  (d) $d = 37.4°$ (3 s.f.)
2 (a) $a = 4.23$ cm (3 s.f.)
  (b) $b = 5.14$ cm (3 s.f.)
  (c) $c = 25.6$ cm (3 s.f.)
  (d) $d = 18.8$ cm (3 s.f.)
  (e) $e = 24.5$ cm (3 s.f.)
  (f) $f = 20.6$ cm (3 s.f.)
3 (a) 6.21 cm (3 s.f.)
  (b) 24.9 cm (3 s.f.)

Exercise 5E

1 (a) $a = 4.12$ cm (3 s.f.)
  (b) $b = 9.12$ cm (3 s.f.)
  (c) $c = 9.53$ cm (3 s.f.)
  (d) $d = 3.60$ cm (3 s.f.)
  (e) $e = 24.2$ cm (3 s.f.)
2 (a) $a = 65.4°$ (3 s.f.)
  (b) $b = 54.3°$ (3 s.f.)
  (c) $c = 41.8°$ (3 s.f.)
  (d) $d = 57.5°$ (3 s.f.)
  (e) $e = 65.3°$ (3 s.f.)
3 Length of rope = 20.6 cm (3 s.f.)

Exercise 5F

1 Height of window above ground = 8.40 m (3 s.f.)
2 Height of tower = 46.9 m (3 s.f.)
3 (a) 22.1 km east (3 s.f.)
  (b) 11.7 km north (3 s.f.)
4 (a) $DC = 14.0$ cm
  (b) $AC = 20.7$ cm
  (c) $AB = 14.79$ cm
  (d) $\angle BDC = 23°$
  (e) $\angle ADB = 33°$ (Lengths to 3 s.f., angles exact)

Exercise 6A

1 (a) $x = 32°$ (sum of angles in triangle = 180°)
  (b) $y = 58°$ (tangent perpendicular to radius)
2 (a) $Q\hat{P}T = 69°$
  (b) $O\hat{P}Q = 21°$
3 (a) $A\hat{T}B = 46°$ (ATB isosceles, sum of angles in triangle = 180°)
  (b) $O\hat{B}A = 23°$ (tangent perpendicular to radius)
4 (a) $P\hat{Q}T = 63°$
  (b) $O\hat{P}Q = 27°$
5 (a) $a = 62°$ (MNT is isosceles, sum of angles in triangle = 180°)
  (b) $b = 31°$ (tangent perpendicular to radius)
6 (a) $a = 39°$ (tangent perpendicular to radius)
  (b) $b = 51°$ (sum of angles in triangle = 180°)

Exercise 6B

1 (i) (a) Area = 256π cm², circumference = 32π cm
      (b) Area = 144π mm², circumference = 24π mm
      (c) Area = 6.86π m², circumference = 5.24π m
      (d) Area = 792.99π m², circumference = 56.32π m
  (ii) (a) Area = 804.25 cm² (2 d.p.),
          circumference = 100.53 cm (2 d.p.)
      (b) Area = 452.39 mm² (2 d.p.),
          circumference = 75.40 mm (2 d.p.)
      (c) Area = 21.57 m² (2 d.p.),
          circumference = 16.46 m (2 d.p.)
      (d) Area = 2491.24 m² (2 d.p.),
          circumerence = 176.93 m (2 d.p.)
2 (a) 2199.1 mm (1 d.p.)
  (b) 109.96 m (2 d.p.)
3 Area = 181.46 cm² (2 d.p.)
4 Area = 907.9 m² (1 d.p.), circumference = 106.8 m (1 d.p.)
5 Diameter = 26.42 m (2 d.p.)
6 Diameter = 1.73 cm (2 d.p.)
7 (i) (a) Area = 8π cm², perimeter = $(8 + 4\pi)$ cm
      (b) Area = 28.125π cm², perimeter$(15 + 7.5\pi)$ cm
      (c) Area = 6.48π cm², perimeter = $(7.2 + 3.6\pi)$ cm
      (d) Area = 3.7538π m², perimeter = $(5.48 + 2.74\pi)$ m
  (ii) (a) Area = 25.13 cm² (2 d.p.), perimeter = 20.57 cm (2 d.p.)
      (b) Area = 88.36 cm² (2 d.p.), perimeter = 38.56 cm (2 d.p.)
      (c) Area = 20.36 cm² (2 d.p.), perimeter = 18.51 cm (2 d.p.)
      (d) Area = 11.79 m² (2 d.p.), perimeter = 14.09 m (2 d.p.)
8 Area = 9.82 m² (2 d.p.), perimeter = 12.86 m (2 d.p.)
9 3.00 cm² (2 d.p.)
10 (a) Area = 8827.43 m² (2 d.p.), perimeter = 388.50 m (2 d.p.)
   (b) Area = 388.36 m² (2 d.p.), perimeter = 78.56 m (2 d.p.)

Exercise 7A

1
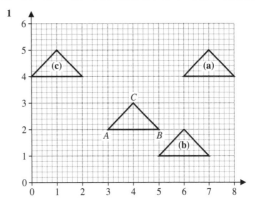

2

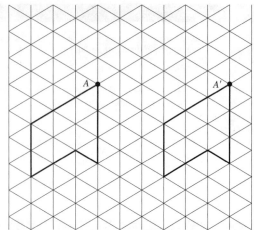

3

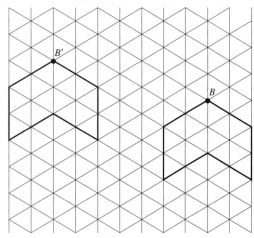

4

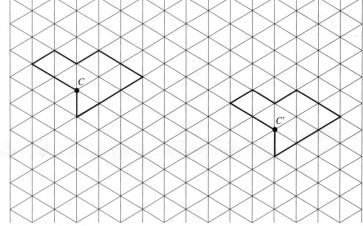

5 (a) Translation onto $\mathbf{A} = \begin{pmatrix} 5 \\ 3 \end{pmatrix}$

Translation onto $\mathbf{B} = \begin{pmatrix} 7 \\ -2 \end{pmatrix}$.

Translation onto $\mathbf{C} = \begin{pmatrix} -7 \\ -5 \end{pmatrix}$

(b) Translation mapping $\mathbf{C}$ onto $\mathbf{B} = \begin{pmatrix} 14 \\ 3 \end{pmatrix}$

(c) Translation mapping $\mathbf{B}$ onto $\mathbf{C} = \begin{pmatrix} -14 \\ -3 \end{pmatrix}$

6

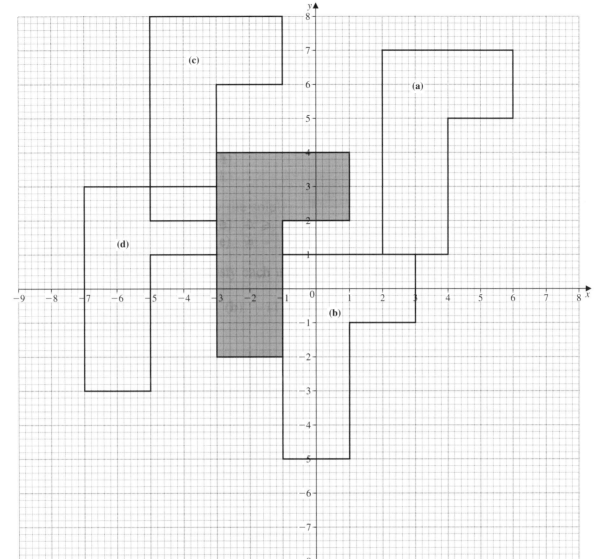

Exercise 7B

1

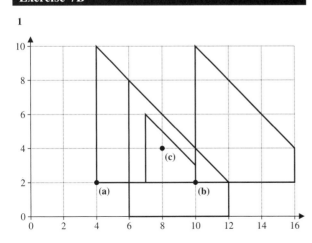

2

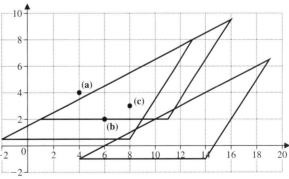

3

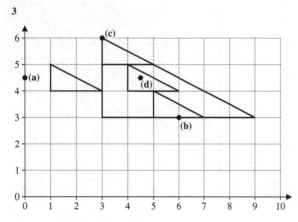

4 (a) (i) Scale factor of enlargement **A** → **B** = $1\frac{1}{2}$
        (ii) Scale factor of enlargement **B** → **A** = $\frac{2}{3}$
   (b) (i) Scale factor of enlargement **A** → **B** = $\frac{1}{2}$
        (ii) Scale factor of enlargement **B** → **A** = 2
5 (a) Centre of enlargement = (5, 2), scale factor = 3
   (b) Centre of enlargement = (11, $3\frac{1}{2}$), scale factor = $\frac{1}{3}$
   (c) Centre of enlargement = (8, −1), scale factor = 2
   (d) Centre of enlargement = (2, 5), scale factor = $1\frac{1}{2}$
6 (a) Centre of enlargement = (6, 8), scale factor = $2\frac{1}{2}$
   (b) Centre of enlargement = (16, 3), scale factor = $1\frac{2}{3}$
   (c) Centre of enlargement = (11, 8), scale factor = $2\frac{1}{2}$
   (d) Centre of enlargement = (−2, 3), scale factor = $1\frac{1}{2}$

7 Perimeter **A** = 20 units, perimeter **E** = 12 units
   A is an enlargement scale factor $2\frac{1}{2}$; perimeter = $2\frac{1}{2} \times 8$
   E is an enlargement scale factor $1\frac{1}{2}$; perimeter = $1\frac{1}{2} \times 8$

Exercise 7C

1 (a) 12 km   (b) 8 km   (c) 10 km
   (d) 5 km   (e) 8.5 km
2

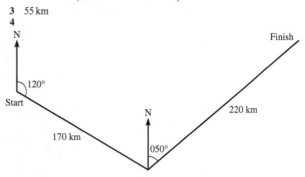

	Ramsey	Castletown	Douglas
Castletown	15.6		
Douglas	10.2	8	
Peel	12.4	9	8.4

(Distances in kilometres)

3 55 km
4

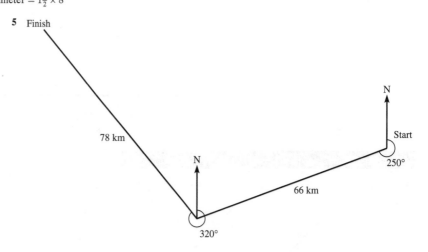

5 Finish

6 (a) Actual size is 25 m by 32.5 m
   (b) Measurements on map are 4 mm wide and 5 cm long
7 Real distances: Brownsea island is 2 km by 1.25 km
                    Bournemouth pier is 225 m long

Exercise 8A

1 (a) Minimum $= 71.5\,\text{cm}$ (b) Minimum $= 15.5\,\text{mm}$
        Maximum $= 72.5\,\text{cm}$ Maximum $= 16.5\,\text{mm}$
    (c) Minimum $= 4.5\,\text{km}$ (d) Minimum $= 99.5\,\text{m}$
        Maximum $= 5.5\,\text{km}$ Maximum $= 100.5\,\text{m}$
2 (a) Minimum $= 49.5\,\text{kg}$ (b) Minimum $= 124.5\,\text{g}$
        Maximum $= 50.5\,\text{kg}$ Maximum $= 125.5\,\text{g}$
    (c) Minimum $= 2.5\,\text{tonnes}$ (d) Minimum $= 81.5\,\text{mg}$
        Maximum $= 3.5\,\text{tonnes}$ Maximum $= 82.5\,\text{mg}$
3 (a) Minimum $= 3.5\,\text{h}$ (b) Minimum $= 22.5\,\text{min}$
        Maximum $= 4.5\,\text{h}$ Maximum $= 23.5\,\text{min}$
    (c) Minimum $= 6.5\,\text{seconds}$ (d) Minimum $= 64.5\,\text{years}$
        Maximum $= 7.5\,\text{seconds}$ Maximum $= 65.5\,\text{years}$
4 (a) Minimum $= 25.5\,^{\circ}\text{C}$ (b) Minimum $= 54.5\,^{\circ}\text{F}$
        Maximum $= 26.5\,^{\circ}\text{C}$ Maximum $= 55.5\,^{\circ}\text{F}$
    (c) Minimum $= 749.5\,\text{m}l$ (d) Minimum $= 7.5\,\text{litres}$
        Maximum $= 750.5\,\text{m}l$ Maximum $= 8.5\,\text{litres}$
5 (a) Minimum $= 259.5\,\text{cm}$ (b) Minimum $= 5.275\,\text{m}$
        Maximum $= 260.5\,\text{cm}$ Maximum $= 5.285\,\text{m}$
    (c) Minimum $= 595\,\text{mm}$ (d) Minimum $= 1995\,\text{mm}$
        Maximum $= 605\,\text{mm}$ Maximum $= 2005\,\text{mm}$
6 (a) $\frac{1}{2}$ hour   (b) $5\,\text{g}$ (c) 7.5 minutes
    (d) $\frac{1}{2}$ second   (e) $25\,\text{cm}$ (f) 0.1 seconds
    (g) $12.5\,\text{m}l$ (h) $2.5\,^{\circ}\text{C}$

Exercise 8B

1 Surface area $= 54\,\text{cm}^2$ 2 Surface area $= 1044\,\text{cm}^2$
3 Surface area $= 246\,\text{cm}^2$ 4 Surface area $= 99\,\text{cm}^2$
5 Surface area $= 85\,\text{cm}^2$ 6 Surface area $= 444\,\text{cm}^2$

Exercise 8C

1 Volume $= 11.25$ litres
2 Volume $= 15.2$ litres (3 s.f.)
3 Volume $= 89.6$ litres (3 s.f.)
4 Volume $= 258.19\,\text{m}^3$ (2 d.p.)
5 Volume $= 3.12$ litres (3 s.f.)
6 Volume $= 525\,\text{cm}^3$
7

	Length	Width	Height	Volume
(a)	4 cm	5 cm	4 cm	$80\,\text{cm}^3$
(b)	12 cm	6 cm	3 cm	$216\,\text{cm}^3$
(c)	1.6 m	10 cm	4 cm	$6400\,\text{cm}^3$
(d)	15 cm	5 min	20 mm	$15\,\text{cm}^3$
(e)	4 m	15 cm	2.2 m	$1.32\,\text{m}^3$
(f)	7 cm	2.5 cm	6 mm	$10.5\,\text{cm}^3$
(g)	2.4 m	15 mm	5 cm	$0.0018\,\text{m}^3$
(h)	3 m	75 mm	3 cm	$6750\,\text{cm}^3$

8 36
9 e.g. $28\,\text{cm} \times 18\,\text{cm} \times 20\,\text{cm}$
10 90

Exercise 8D

1 (a) $27\,\text{cm}^3$
    (b) $2040\,\text{cm}^3$
    (c) $216\,\text{cm}^3$
    (d) $63\,\text{cm}^3$
2 $739\,760\,\text{cm}^3$
3 $10\,080\,\text{cm}^3$
4 $12\,000\,\text{cm}^3$
5 $260\,\text{m}^3$

Exercise 8E

1 $376.99\,\text{cm}^2$ (2 d.p.)
2 (a) (i) $6361.73\,\text{cm}^2$ (2 d.p.)
        (ii) $6488.96\,\text{cm}^2$ (2 d.p.)
        (iii) $14\,313.88\,\text{cm}^3$ (2 d.p.)
    (b) (i) $1507.96\,\text{cm}^2$ (2 d.p.)
        (ii) $1517.01\,\text{cm}^2$ (2 d.p.)
        (iii) $904.78\,\text{cm}^3$ (2 d.p.)
    (c) (i) $2827.43\,\text{mm}^2$ (2 d.p.)
        (ii) $3180.86\,\text{mm}^2$ (2 d.p.)
        (iii) $10\,602.88\,\text{mm}^3$ (2 d.p.)
    (d) (i) $376.99\,\text{mm}^2$ (2 d.p.)
        (ii) $1790.71\,\text{mm}^2$ (2 d.p.)
        (iii) $2827.43\,\text{mm}^3$ (2 d.p.)
3 $1.98\,\text{cm}$ (2 d.p.)
4 $0.63\,\text{cm}$ (2 d.p.)
5 $301\,592.89\,\text{cm}^3$ (2 d.p.)

Exercise 8F

1 40 km per hour
2 45 km
3 164 km per hour (3 s.f.)
4 108 km
5 (a) $82.7\,\text{m s}^{-1}$ (3 s.f.)
    (b) 298 km per hour (3 s.f.)
6 266.5 m apart (4 s.f.)
7 $804\,\text{cm}^3$ (3 s.f.)
8 $2.5\,\text{g per cm}^3$
9 91.44 g
10

Substance	Mass	Volume	Density
Hydrogen	900 000 tonnes	$1\,\text{km}^3$	$0.0009\,\text{g/cm}^3$
Air	20 kg	$15.38\,\text{m}^3$	$0.0013\,\text{g/cm}^3$
Aluminium	15.3 kg	$41\,300\,\text{cm}^3$	$0.375\,\text{g/cm}^3$

11 Density of dish $= 11.7\,\text{g/cm}^3$, so it is unlikely that the dish is solid silver.
12 $0.17\,\text{cm}^3$ (2 d.p.)

Exercise 9A

1 (a) 200 times
    (b) 600 times
    (c) 400 times
2 (a) (i) $\frac{31}{300}$
        (ii) $\frac{269}{300}$
    (b) 265 417
3 (a) Spinning the spinner is an event governed by the laws of chance and so the outcomes are determined by laws of probability. It is likely that repeating the same experiment will not give the same results so we will get a different set of outcomes.
    (b) Estimate for probability of stopping on
        (i) B is $\frac{37}{150}$ (ii) D is $\frac{1}{10}$ (iii) a vowel is $\frac{8}{25}$
4 Estimate for the likely number of times spinner will stop on C is 204.
5 If the spinner was not biased we would have $P(A) = P(B) = P(C) = P(D) = P(E) = 0.2$ i.e. we would expect each letter to come up about 2000 times. In fact, B came up 4009 times, A 593 times and C 1427 times, which suggests the spinner is biased in favour of B. It appears to be biased against A and, to a lesser degree, C.

Exercise 9B

1 (a) and (c)

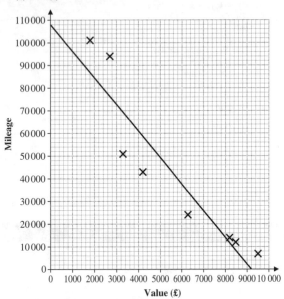

(b) Correlation between mileage and value is negative
(d) (i) 50 000
  (ii) £3100
2 (a) zero
  (b) positive
  (c) negative
  (d) negative
3 Many possibilities e.g.
  (a) Marks students got in a Maths exam and a Science exam would be positively correlated.
  (b) The number of hours of sunshine in a day and the amount of rainfall in a day would be negatively correlated.
4 (a) and (c)

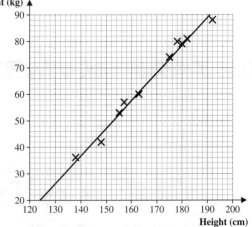

(b) Positive correlation between height and weight of a person.
(d) (i) 47 kg
  (ii) 174 cm

Exercise 10A

1

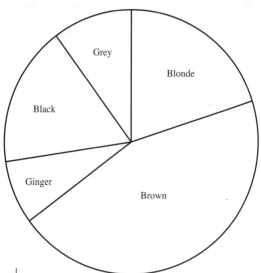

2

0	6 8
1	2 5 6 7 9
2	0 2 5 6 7 7 9 9
3	1 2 2 3 3 4 6 8 8 8 9
4	0 1 2 2 4 5 6 6 6 6 8 8 9 9
5	0 1 2 2 2 3 4 4 6 6 7 9
6	1 1 1 4 4
7	0 3
8	2

3

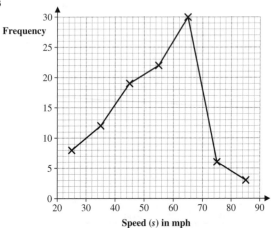

4

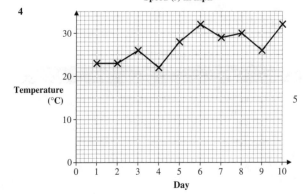

5

5

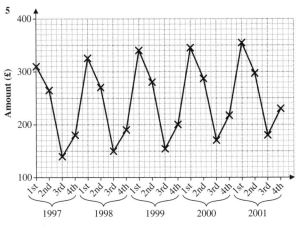

6

90	9
100	9
110	0 0 0 1 5 8
120	0 0 5 5 5 7 7
130	2 4
140	1 9
150	9
160	3 9
170	0
180	0

7

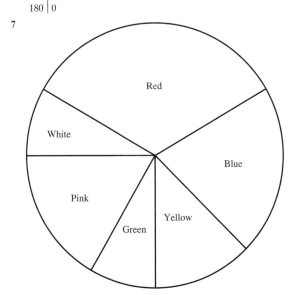

8

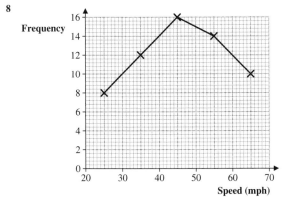

9

40	3 3 8 9
50	1 3 7 8
60	0 2 4 8 8 8 9
70	0 2 5 7
80	1 1 2 4
90	1 2 8
100	1 2
110	3 7

10

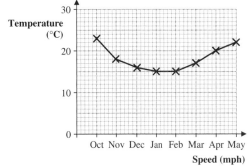

11

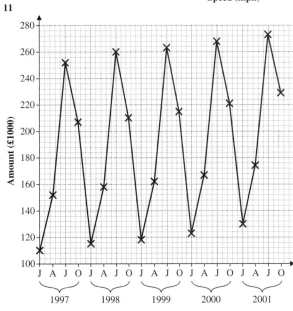

12

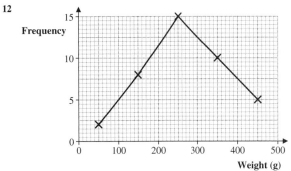

13

Weight (w) in kg	Frequency
$40 < w \leqslant 50$	4
$50 < w \leqslant 60$	6
$60 < w \leqslant 70$	4
$70 < w \leqslant 80$	7
$80 < w \leqslant 90$	6

14

Colour	Frequency
Yellow	18
Black	12
Red	30
Blue	20
Green	40

15

```
 0 | 3 4 4 5 6 8 8 8 8 9 9 9
10 | 0 1 1 2 2 2 3 4 4 5 5 5 6 6 6 7 7 7 7 8
20 | 0 1 1 2 2 3 4 7
30 | 0 2 2 8
40 | 0 2 7
50 | 1 2 7
```

16

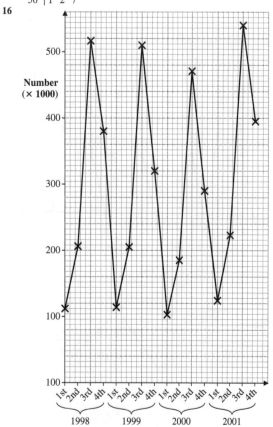

Exercise 10B

1 (a) Estimate for mean weight $= 255$ g

2 (a) Estimate for mean number of hours worked $= 58.25$ hours

(b)

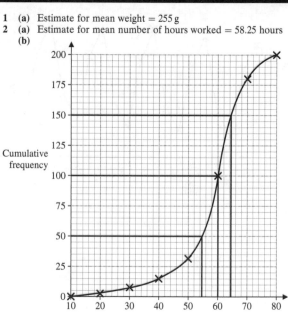

(c) (i) Median $= 60$ hours
(ii) Interquartile range $= 9$ hours

(d)

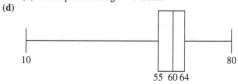

3

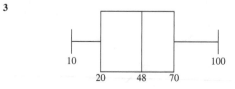

4 (a)

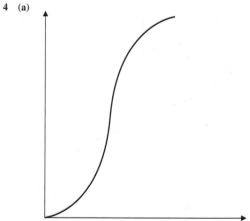

(b)

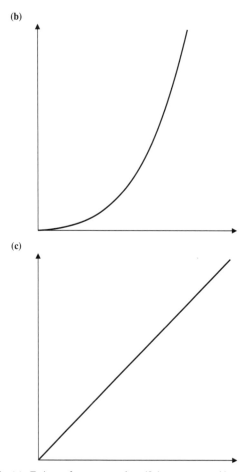

(c)

5 (a) Estimate for mean mark = 49 (to nearest mark)

(b)

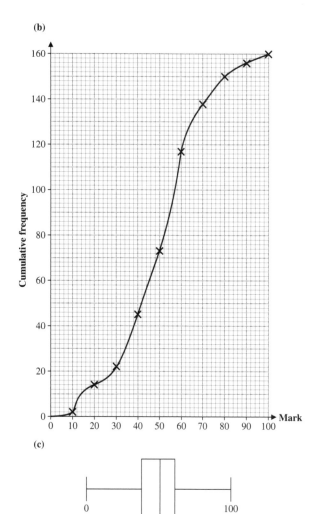

(c)

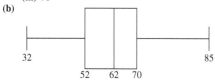

Number of students who passed = 102

6 (a) (i) 62
(ii) 52
(iii) 70

(b)

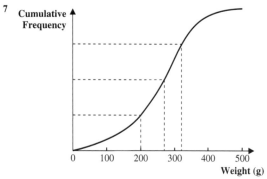

7 Cumulative Frequency

8 (a) (i) 58
(ii) 32

(b)

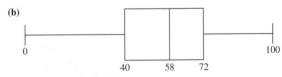

40   58   72

(c) Estimate $= 2000 - 530 = 1470$

Exercise 10C

1   It is not possible to conclude that, in general, the girls did better than the boys. We need more information about the marks, for example the spread of the marks. It could be that the majority of the boys got higher marks than the maximum girl mark, but some boys did very badly and so brought the average mark down. e.g. 3 girls all get 50, so average $= 50$ and of 3 boys, 2 get 70 marks, 1 gets 4 so boys' average $= 48$ which is lower than the girls though 2 of the boys did better than all 3 girls.

2   Most of the students at Lucea did better than those at Jordan Hill. No student at Jordan Hill got more than half marks. There are some students at Jordan Hill who did slightly better than some of the students from Lucea.

3   The general correlation is positive, so that the more hours work a person does the more money they are likely to get. These results show an exception, an outlier; this could be a managing director's job, so they will get paid a lot more for fewer hours worked.

4   The mean weight must lie between the minimum and maximum weights – in this case between 0 g and 500 g. Therefore a mean of 2840 g must be incorrect.

5   Gary generally has more cars at a particular range than Nick; an exception to this is for cars of value £0–£2000.
The price range where the difference in the number of cars they have is greatest, is £8000–£9000.
The price range where the difference in the number of cars they have is smallest, is £7000–£8000.

Examination style practice paper

Section 1

1   **(a)** 8000
    (b) $3 \left(\frac{400 \times 60}{8000}\right) \simeq 3$

2   **(a)** 26
    (b) $A = 5f + 10t$

3   Translation $\left(\begin{smallmatrix} 3 \\ -2 \end{smallmatrix}\right)$

4   **(a)** $x \geqslant -1\frac{1}{2}$
    (b)

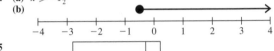

5

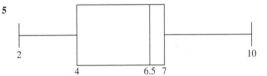

4   6.5 7

6   **(a)** 7×10^{-3}
    (b) 8×10^4

Section 2

1   **(a)** $\frac{1}{9}$
    (b) $\frac{5}{9}$

2   **(a)** Scale factor $= 3$
    (b) $x = 9$
    (c) $y = 57$

3   $1 : 3$

4   Area $= 63.6 \, \text{cm}^2$ (3 s.f.)

5   0.0476 (3 s.f.)

6   **(a)** $x^2 - 9x + 20$
    (b) $(x - 2)(x + 6)$

7   $AB = 5.88 \, \text{cm}$ (3 s.f.)